THE FIFTH ELEMENT

THE FIFTH ELEMENT

The Rainbow Bridge between the Dimensions

Salah-Eddin Gherbi

Acknowledgments

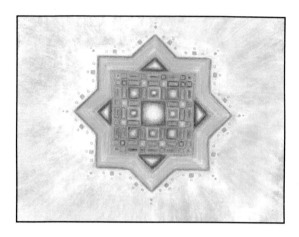

Artistic expression of the Alton Priors crop circle

I am grateful to the divine universe and wonderful support from the community of people in Glastonbury who helped me to put my message out there.

Many thanks to my musician friend Michael Tyack for supporting me on my path and editing, and proofreading of the book, my friend Holly Rosewood for further proofreading, Rob Macbeth for keeping me grounded in the garden of Paddington Farm in Glastonbury. My friend Hannamari Mäkelä for sharing her beautiful drawings of crop circles, and all the wonderful friends around me, without whom the epic task of compiling this book would not have been possible.

Many thanks to Sue Cawthorne for revising the first edition of my book, giving birth to a second edition with further additional material.

I would like to thank all the kind people who gave their permission for me to reproduce their photographic images, whose names I have listed at the end of the book.

The information and insights presented in this book have been collated over the past four years whilst living in the holy land of Glastonbury. I am grateful for support from my own divine guidance and to Mother Earth.

"We are all connected in the magnificence of the Divine Blueprint"

"We are all the expression of the Divine Beauty"

Salah-Eddin Gherbi

Content

Foreword

The Rainbow Bridge is the bridge between Heaven and Earth. It is the universal unified field between the dimensions, which connects all things and all nations together beyond differenciation.

As a meditative person, I have always contemplated the stars in the sky and how they perfectly follow the principle of order. In this book I present an alternative theory unifying matter and spirit through the language of numbers and geometry, opening new doorways in physics and mathematics; and promoting unity in all things. I have always believed that profound knowledge can come from within.

Undoubtedly, we are all connected with each other beyond duality or any form of separation within our minds. Geometry is a tangible field which allows us to unify the intellect and the heart. In my work I aim to feel a connection to the core of my heart whilst using the logical part of my brain, having worked through the first year of a Master's degree in Astrophysics.

Many of the harmonic numbers in our known reality were encoded in the Bible. My work shows the connection of all things through the fifth element or *ether*, which dictates the behavior of the four fundamental interactions in physics - Electromagnetism, Gravity, Strong and Weak nuclear forces. The fifth force or pyramid energy is not currently considered by mainstream science. It is my belief that each being possesses an inner alchemical fire that allows us to connect with the One Quintessence.

We are now entering a new era with energies shifting to a higher frequency. The coming of this new era was recorded by the Mayan civilization as the time of a New Sun. Many prophecies have spoken about the coming of a golden age when nations will be united again. Indeed, the end of the thirteen Baktun cycle is upon us. We are all experiencing beautiful changes in this exciting time.

The Ancient Mexican Stone of the Sun

> "There manifests itself in the fully developed being, Man, a desire mysterious, inscrutable and irresistible: to imitate nature, to create, to work himself the wonders he perceives.... Long ago he recognized that all perceptible matter comes from a primary substance, or tenuity beyond conception, filling all space, the Akasha or luminiferous ether, which is acted upon by the life giving Prana or creative force, calling into existence, in never ending cycles all things and phenomena. The primary substance, thrown into infinitesimal whirls of prodigious velocity, becomes gross matter; the force subsiding, the motion ceases and matter disappears, reverting to the primary substance."
>
> **Nikola Tesla, from "Man's Greatest Achievement"**

> "Only the existence of a field of force can account for the motions of the bodies as observed, and its assumption dispenses with space curvature. All literature on this subject is futile and destined to oblivion. So are all attempts to explain the workings of the universe without recognizing the existence of the ether and the indispensable function it plays in the phenomena. My second discovery was of a physical truth of the greatest importance. As I have searched the entire scientific records in more than a half dozen languages for a long time without finding the least anticipation, I consider myself the original discoverer of this truth, which can be expressed by the statement: There is no energy in matter other than that received from the environment."
>
> **Excerpt from Tesla's prepared statement for his 81st birthday (July 10, 1937)**

0. Introduction

There was a time when a High priest was a scientist and a scientist was a High priest. There was no separation between the contemplation of the Universe, geometry, metrology and the field of spiritual practice including silent meditation. Man's journey was in perfect harmony with the One Quintessence. At that time *Atlantis* and other civilizations such as *Mu* and *Lemuria* were highly advanced and inhabited by brilliant scientists and highly evolved spiritual beings.

This book presents a unified theory of science, metaphysics, the philosophy of divine nature and geometry, encoding harmonic numbers from the Bible, folklore and ancient scriptures, revealing a unique template uniting microcosm with macrocosm.

"All is Number" **Pythagoras**

Crop circles formed in the last few years of the twentieth century have brought forward numerical and geometrical keys, revealing the behaviour of divine creation and the *New Jerusalem.* The profound nature of these crop circles has revealed further aspects, of our multi-dimensional nature within the Universe.

A particular crop circle which appeared in Hackpen Hill, Wiltshire, in 2012, a Hypercube reveals important harmonic numbers which are found in ancient Calendars, temples and nature. These numbers are the blueprint of a universal language appearing in every field of study.

Through numbers encoded in the Great Pyramid of Giza in Egypt and the Temple of Solomon heralded by Ezekiel in the Bible, this book emphasizes the musical aspect of numbers strengthening the importance of the number 432 as a reference pitch, when tuning instruments. Divine numbers resonate throughout the construct of creation.

Although the book unavoidably uses the language of mathematical formulae, equations can be ignored by non mathematicians as the essence of the topic can be captured from the many diagrams.

The ideas presented are a product of deep meditative reflection combined with my mathematics background and inner insights. I encourage readers to take their time when reading this book. It may require a gradual assimilation to grasp the scope and depth of the many layers of content, spanning mathematics, astronomy, geometry, sound, architecture, numerology and music, plus modern and ancient wisdom. Above all, I see this book as the beginning of a greater work in progress and is not a conclusion in and of itself.

This book will illustrate how Glastonbury Abbey, Stonehenge, Lord Jesus Christ and the diameter of the Moon are related by numbers. It posits that numbers are instructions given to our manifest three dimensional world through the spiritual plane. Geometry can be seen as one expression of these numbers as they take form through our multidimensional landscape.

This work aims to support and accompany anyone involved in what I perceive to be an evolutionary process taking place in our collective consciousness. We are approaching a time when we will remember the connection of all things macro and micro and between the body of Mother Earth and the Cosmos. It is an urge for humankind to break down all ideas of separation and to strengthen the experience of embodying Oneness that naturally prevails.

The final pages contain some useful reference sections :

- *Appendix* details the mathematical and astronomical constants defined and referenced.
- *Crop Circles* presents crop circles in larger images for clearer examination.
- *Gematria* lists the relevant Hebrew or Greek words from the Old and New Testament, used to infer numerological relationship to the underlying concepts that are interwoven throughout the book.
- *The Temple of Solomon* presents the ground plan of the Temple as described by Ezekiel in the Bible. I will shows how the Temple is a reflection of an important piece of the *Etheric Particle* from where emanates an accumulation of etheric energy expressed geometrically and mathematically through the spiral in nature otherwise known as the *Fibonacci spiral*.

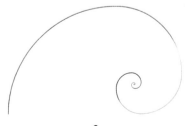

1. The Tetractys

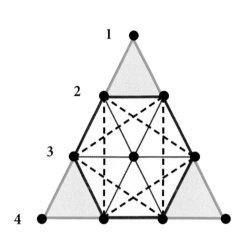

Fig. 1.1
The Tetractys.

The Tetractys is the foundation stone of Divine Architecture. It held an important mystical meaning to the Pythagoreans who considered it to be the basis of structure of the Universe in terms of arithmetic, music and geometry. The Tetractys means literally "the number four" and is a triangle composed of **10** points rising upwards, arranged in four rows. The number ten is mathematically known as the fourth "triangular number" with rows of one, two, three and four points. Each row has an important meaning and brings forward an understanding of the connection between the innermost and the outermost.

The first harmonic number encoded in the *Tetractys* is **432**, a cosmic code which can be read from the base to the top of a step pyramid, such as the ones found in central America. This is another form of pyramid with a flat top (Fig. 1.5). The harmonic number **432** rises from the base upwards. This is a very important number when tuning instruments to resonate with consciousness. **432** is the *gematria value* for 'All things' (παντα[2]) in Greek. From planetary systems to atoms. Everything surrounding us is an embodiment of perfect harmony created by numbers, referred to in music as "Harmonics".

The *Tetractys* representing the organization of space from a two dimensional view.

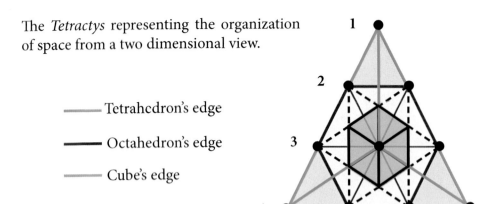

——— Tetrahedron's edge

——— Octahedron's edge

——— Cube's edge

Fig. 1.2
The Fundamental solids.

First row : From a single original point everything is created and brought into existence from nothingness. This could be considered as a state of awareness to that which is about to manifest into creation.

Second row : From a single point two further points are generated defining the first dimension. The possibility of going from one point to another brings the idea of motion into consciousness.

Third row : A line drawn between these three dots defines the second dimension. Structure is formed into consciousness with the possibility of quantification and measurement.

Fourth row : A line drawn between these four dots defines the third dimension where geometry takes form. From this triangle all regular polygons can be generated, such as the square, the pentagon, the hexagon etc.

Other fundamental blocks can be built from the original block. The first solid appearing is the projection of the tetrahedron shown in light blue. The red hexagon represents the projection of the octahedron with the green cube projected inside.

The Tetrahedron	The Octahedron	The Cube

720 degrees	1,440 degrees	2,160 degrees
4 faces, 4 vertices	8 faces, 6 vertices	6 faces, 8 vertices

Fig. 1.3

Platonic solids emerging from the Tetractys.

The numbers encoded in these solids are harmonic. The peculiar quality of these numbers is they all add up to **9**.

$$7 + 2 + 0 = 9 \qquad 1 + 4 + 4 + 0 = 9 \qquad 2 + 1 + 6 + 0 = 9$$

The number **9** is an important pillar in the structure of space-time and acts uniquely in the system of numbers. Below is a table listing some musical notes. Notes are based on a D scale from **144 Hz**.

Geometry	Angles °	Freq Hz	Notes	Ratios
Tetrahedron	720	720	Major 3rd F#	5:4
Octahedron	1,440	1,440	Major 3rd F#	5:4
Cube	2,160	2,160	Major 7th C#	15:8
Cell (Fig. 1.7)	3,240	3,240	Just tritone G#	45:32
Rhombic Dode	4,320	4,320	Just tritone G#	45:32
Icosahedron	3,600	3,600	B♭	25:16
Dodecahedron	6,480	6,480	Just tritone G#	45:32

Fig. 1.4

Musical notes of the solids.

"Music is geometry in time."[3] **Arthur Honegger**

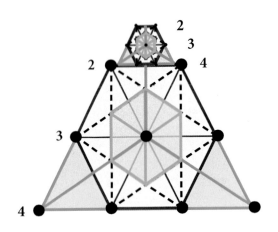

The step pyramids in Central America and Egypt come from the geometry of the *Tetractys*.

A second *Tetractys* is placed on the top of the first as a fractal forming the second step.

The numerical sequence **432 432** ... rises from the base upwards.

Fig. 1.5
The Tetractys and step pyramids.

Fig. 1.6
Step Pyramid of Djoser.

Constructed at Saqqara about 4,700 years ago and attributed to Imhotep. The pyramid stood **203** ft tall, with a base of **358** ft x **410** ft and clad in polished white stone.

Fig. 1.7
The *Temple of Kukulkan.*

A **79**-ft-high pyramid in southeast Mexico with **9** layers and a square base with sides measuring **181** ft. There are **4** stairways each with **91** steps making a total of **364** steps, the exact number of days in a lunar year.

Added to the base platform, the total comes to **365**, the number of days in a solar year.

The icosahedron and dodecahedron are both dual platonic solids. The icosahedron can be placed inside the dodecahedron and vice versa. One has **20** faces with **12** vertices and the other has **12** faces with **20** vertices.

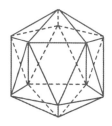

Fig. 1.8
Icosahedron
and Dodecahedron

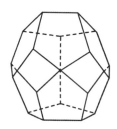

The Icosahedron

20 triangular faces
12 vertices, **3,600** degrees

The Dodecahedron

12 pentagonal faces
20 vertices, **6,480** degrees

The *rhombic dodecahedron* has **4,320** degrees and is made from **12** rhombus. The sum of the four angles of a rhombus is always **360** degrees. The *rhombic dodecahedron* appears in nature in the structure of the honeycomb cells. At the top is a pyramid made from three blue rhombus closing the end of the cell. The opening is a red hexagon prism at the bottom joining to the top with six green trapezes. Each cell is called "half of a *rhombic dodecahedron*". The sum of the angles is **3,240** degrees, again adding up to **9**.

$$3 + 2 + 4 + 0 = 9$$

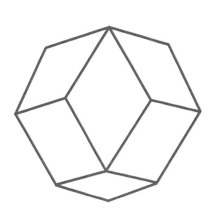

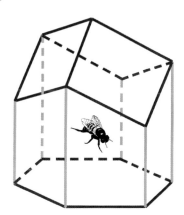

Fig. 1.9
Rhombic dodecahedron (left) and the cell of a honey comb (right).

These fundamental blocs appear in nature in the structure of crystals and the five natural elements; earth, air, fire, water and the quintessence of the heavens (ether). Each of them is associated with a platonic solid. Earth is associated with the cube, air with the octahedron, water with the icosahedron, fire with the tetrahedron and ether with the dodecahedron. The heavenly bodies were encoded in the Great Pyramid of Giza through the number 7.

Another key number is **5,040**, the Earth's radius in miles **3,960** added to the Moon's radius **1,080**. The number **5,040** carried an important metaphysical meaning to early civilizations.

$$7! = 7 \times 6 \times 5 \times 4 \times 3 \times 2 \times 1 = 5040$$

The fifth element, or ether, is a subtle medium through which the celestial bodies move in harmony. This element encourages the prosperity of life and order in nature. Entropy is the measure of disorder in any process. The Second Law of Thermodynamics stipulates that *"the entropy of the universe increases during any spontaneous process"*, which contradicts the orderly celestial signature described by the heavenly bodies.

As a consequence of the Second Law of Thermodynamics only technologies based on explosion and destruction are explored. When the ether is considered, the second law must be dismissed, allowing further explorations into technologies based on implosion and harmony of life.

The beautiful geometric patterns found in nature are a direct expression of the *ether* or *'The All'* which orchestrates order in the universe through sound, light, numbers and geometry. In the past physical objects were considered to be connected to their *essence* in the subtle world. Philosophy, Art and Mathematics were studied with an awareness of the divine transcendental connection of the soul on the earthly plane to the One Quintessence.

The Pythagoreans for example considered reality as 'mathematically describable'. The practice of philosophy aided the transformation of the soul and a connection to a divine order through the science of numbers.

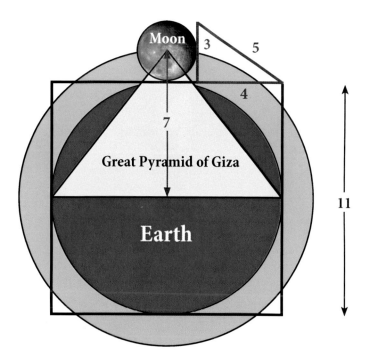

Fig. 1.10.
Earth and Moon embodied within the Great Pyramid.

In Figure 1.10 the Great Pyramid has an approximately square base with a perimeter equal to the circumference of a circle with radius equal to its height.

The dimensions of the Great Pyramid incorporate measurements from which can be calculated :

- The dimensions of the Earth and Moon.
- The radius ratio between the Earth and Moon.
- The Pythagorean Triangle **3 - 4 - 5**.

The pyramid builders appear to have been advanced astronomers.

> *"Few things in this world are more predictable than the reaction of conventional minds to unconventional ideas."* **John Anthony West**

Fig. 1.11
Top view of the Great Pyramid of Giza.

The base of the Great Pyramid is not a perfect square. Each side is slightly concaved. This must be an important factor in its function as an etheric energy device, considering that energy waves are based on hyperbolic geometry.

Fig. 1.12
The geometric construction of the octagon.

The left diagram shows the construction of the octagon in straight lines and the right diagram shows the construction of a curved octagon representing hyperbolic geometry.

The *music of the heavens* was believed to be describable through numbers and geometry with a system of codes originating from the fundamental structure of space-time. The pyramid builders taught that relationships between all things can be expressed through geometry and numbers.

Music tuned with these harmonic numbers is a way of expressing resonance within the geometric construct of the universe. The Great Pyramid of Giza is one of the most famous examples of musical architecture since the ratio between Earth and Moon's radius (**11÷3**) is a seventh of **528 Hz** on a scale from D at **288 Hz**.

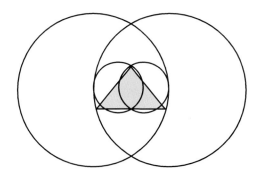

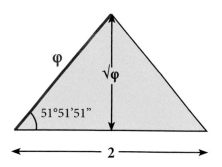

Fig. 1.13
The Vesica Piscis
containing the Great Pyramid.

Fig. 1.14
The dimensions of the Great Pyramid
with Phi (φ) **1.618**.

A first *Vesica Piscis* is built and contained in the center of a larger *Vesica Piscis*.

The base leg is **2**, the slope side is the *Golden Ratio Phi* (φ **1.618**) and the height is the square root of *Phi* (√φ). The Great Pyramid has four faces with a *golden angle* of inclination **51° 51' 51"** or **51.84°**.

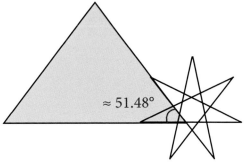

Fig. 1.15
The seven-pointed star
and the Great Pyramid.

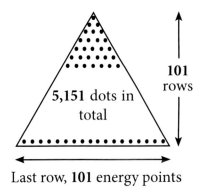

Last row, **101** energy points

Fig. 1.16
The triangular number 101

The angle of a seven-pointed star **51.48** degrees is closely related to the slope angle of the Great Pyramid **51.84** degrees through the language of numbers.

5,151 dots embodies the slope angle in degrees and minutes (**51°51'**) of the Great Pyramid.

"*The pyramid retains many mysteries, most obviously in its construction; its standards of craft and engineering are inexplicable to modern experts. As a monumental record, however, it is a true product of its age, a summary of esoteric code of numbers and proportions that, according to Plato in the Laws, maintained the high civilization of Egypt unchanged 'for at least ten thousand years'. That sounds like a science worthy of the name. The ancient monument builders of Egypt and elsewhere were obviously familiar with the mathematical constants such as Pi (π) and Phi (φ) in their units of measurement is clear proof that they had precise knowledge of the earth's dimensions.*"[3]

John Michell with Allan Brown

Fig. 1.17
The Great Pyramid.

2. Pyramid Energy

Pyramid Energy could be described as the accumulation of standing wave interference inside a pyramid emanating *Golden Spirals* or vortexes.

To the monks of early Christianity the geometry of the square symbolized the creation of the structured universe and how the number two, the infinite and finite, can be generated from the one. In ancient Israel King Solomon described the passage from one to two as a reference to 'Divine Inscrutability'.

Our physical reality is based on the pillar number four, with the four elements of air, earth, fire and water, the four directions and four corners of Earth. The *Tetractys*, meaning 'the number four' is the tetrahedron in three dimensions with four triangular faces (Figs. 1.2 and 1.3). It is the first polygonal solid and the fundamental structure of space-time. Geometry is the key to understanding the multi-layered universe and a doorway to the study of the divine order of nature. A single point represents 'Unity' or 'the One' and can also represent the circle or the square. Square grids are created in the following manner.

1. From the One is born the Essence of Duality, the passage from One to Two, which also symbolizes the Three in One. A square or a circle with a single point in the center is equivalent to 'Unity' or 'the One' and the pure inseparable essence of all things in Oneness. The Primary Grid **1 x 1** is the simple square.
2. The Secondary Grid **1 x 1** is constructed by drawing diagonals through a single point at the center.
3. The center provides the four coordinates for the division of the sides of the square bringing the Tertiary Grid **1 x 1** or cross, which in ancient times was regarded as a symbol of the Trinity or Three in One.

The three together produce a **2 x 2** Primary Grid. From a **2 x 2** Grid, a **4 x 4** Grid is built through the same steps. This construction was the template for designing Celtic decorative knots in ancient times.

The Primary Grid **1 x 1**

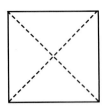

The Secondary Grid **1 x 1**

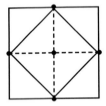

The Tertiary Grid **1 x 1**
Red diamond

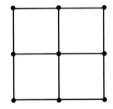

The Primary Grid **2 x 2**

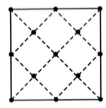

The Secondary Grid **2 x 2**

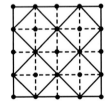

The Tertiary Grid **2 x 2**
Red diamonds

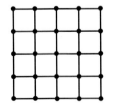

The Primary Grid **4 x 4**

Fig. 2.1
Geometric construction from primary grids 1 x 1 to 4 x 4.

Pyramid Energy can also be understood through an expanded fractal of squares revealed in a crop circle at East Field Alton Priors, Wiltshire, United Kingdom on 3rd July 2005. The Alton Priors crop circle is based on a four by four grid of square units clearly visible at its center.

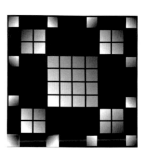

Fig. 2.2
The Alton Priors Crop Circle displaying Fractal 44.

The Primary Grid **4 x 4** is seen at the center of the Alton Priors crop circle. Four **2 x 2** Grids are placed on each corner of the **4 x 4** Grid. Finally twelve single squares are placed on each corner of the **2 x 2** Grid, bringing a total of **44** squares.

Fractal 44 can be viewed as a **12 x 12** Grid representing the base of a pyramid with four *Zero Energy Points* through which operate the four creative forces. The Universe is ordered through the *ether* governing the four fundamental forces. Universal motion or spin originates from the *ether* working through the four forces on any scale from galaxies to atoms.

Binary codes bring important information about the numerical structure of the pyramid. Different sized squares and rectangles appear in the shaded areas. A binary code appears if we consider the yellow rectangle equal to **1** and the green square equal to **0**. Binary codes can be read from either left to right or up and down.

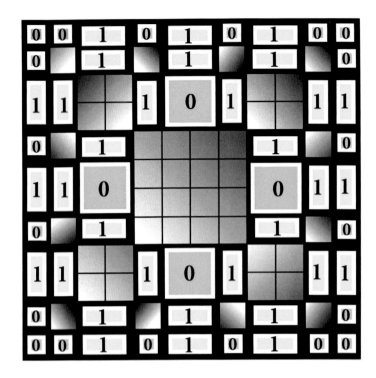

Fig. 2.3 *Binary codes around Fractal 44.*

$0110 = 6$

$01110 = 14 = 7 \times 2$

$110011 = 51 = 17 \times 3$

$001010100 = 84 = 7 \times 12$

$1110111 = 119 = 7 \times 17$

- **6** suggests the **6 x 6 x 6** Cube.
- **7** appears as the height of the Great Pyramid in relation to its base.
- **51** appears in the slope angle of the Great Pyramid and the seven pointed star.
- **84** refers to one of the possible resonant frequencies of the Great Pyramid in Hertz.
- **119** brings again the number **7** in its divisors.

On each side of the **4 x 4** grid is a **101** doorway.

The number **101** represents a 'zero gateway' with **1**'s on either side, emanating *Zero Point Energy* from the zero. The triangular number **101** is linked to the Great Pyramid (Fig. 1.13).

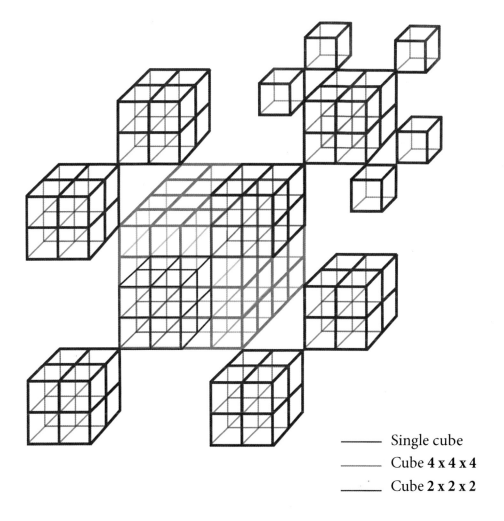

——— Single cube
——— Cube **4 x 4 x 4**
——— Cube **2 x 2 x 2**

Fig. 2.4 *Fractal 44 from a three dimensional view.*

Fractal 44 is a template unifying the microcosm and macrocosm and a blueprint of the Divine Architecture.

Fractal 44 consists of **184** cubes in three dimensions with a **4 x 4 x 4** orange cube at its center composed of **64** cubes. Eight blue cubes of **2 x 2 x 2** sit at each corner bringing a total of **128** cubes (**64 + 64 = 128**). Finally individual red cubes are placed on the corners of the **2 x 2 x 2** blue cubes adding a further **56** cubes (**7 x 8**) resulting in a total of **184** cubes (**128 + 56 = 184**). There are only seven red cubes placed around the blue bloc as the **8**th red cube is integrated into the **4 x 4 x 4** orange bloc of **64** cubes.

Fig. 2.5
Egyptian Ankh.

Fig. 2.6
The sacred symbol of Mu.

Fig. 2.7
Celtic Cross.

Ancient civilizations represented the number **101** with a symbol showing four directions. These include the Egyptian *Ankh*, the Key of universal motion from the lost continent of Mu and the Celtic cross. The spiral at the center of the sacred symbol of Mu shows the nature of motion to be a spinning spiral suggesting a degree of torsion effect. The Ankh is a cross meaning '*Life or Soul*'. The six faces of the cube can be unfolded to form a cross. The vertical axis consists of four squares expressing the four elemental forces and the horizontal axis of three squares expressing unmanifested action.

The cross represents the four Arms of God operating throughout the microcosm and macrocosm linking the manifested and unmanifested worlds. A symbol of life, unity and stability.

"*The mathematical sciences particularly exhibit order, symmetry, and limitation, and these are the greatest form of the beautiful.*"[1]

Aristotle

"*Geometry existed before the creation. It is co-eternal with the mind of God…Geometry provided God with a model for the Creation…*"

Johannes Kepler

Fig. 2.8
The camp of the Israelites.

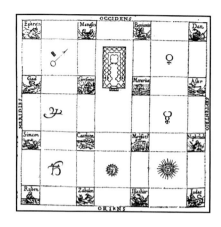

The camp of the Israelites around the Tabernacle was described in a book called *'Ezechielem Explanationes et Apparatus Vrbis Templi Hierosolymitani'* by the author and architect *Juan Bautista Villalpando.*

Fractal 44 geometrically fits with the camp of the Israelites.

In comparison with Figure 2.8, Figure 2.10 shows twelve white squares representing the twelve tribes of Israel. The four colored squares on the corners of the **4 x 4** grid are the four *Levites* tribes of *Merari, Moses* and *Aaron, Caath* and *Gerfon,* respectively symbols of the four elements, Earth, Air, Fire and Water.

The *ether* or fifth element represents *'the All',* the spirit element from which everything is born including the four elements. The tabernacle is located on one of the four **101** *Zero Energy Point* 'gateways' and generates this spiralling energy.

Tribes	Forces	Zodiacal signs	Elements
Ephraim	Gravity	Taurus	Earth
Ruben	Weak Nuclear	Aquarius	Air
Judah	Electromagnetism	Leo	Fire
Dan	Strong Nuclear	Scorpio	Water
All of them	*Pyramid Energy*	All of them	Ether

Fig. 2.9 *Relationships between the tribes of Israel, interactive forces, Zodiacal Signs (Fig. 2.11) and the elements.*

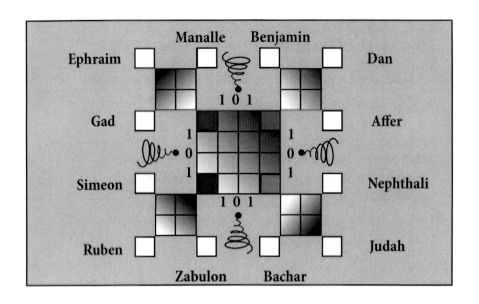

Fig. 2.10 *Fractal 44 and the camp of the Israelites.*

■ **Caath, Fire**	■ **Gerfon, Water**	🌀 Spiralling Energy
■ **Merari, Earth**	■ **Moses, Aaron, Air**	• *Zero Energy Point*

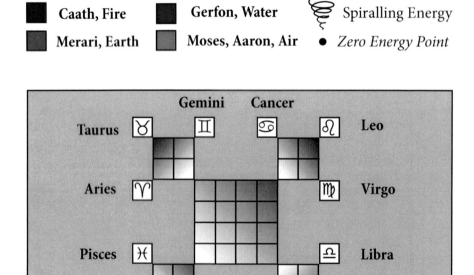

Fig. 2.11 *Fractal 44 and the twelve Zodiacal Signs.*

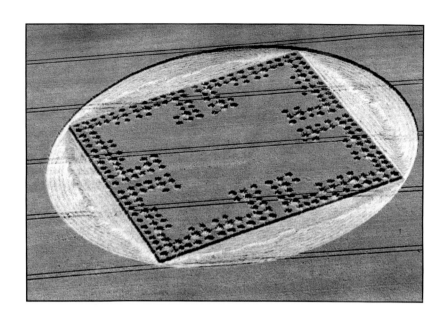

Fig. 2.12
Crop circle formation, Windmill Hill, Wiltshire, 19ᵗʰ July 1999.

"Geometry is knowledge of the eternally existent." **Pythagoras**

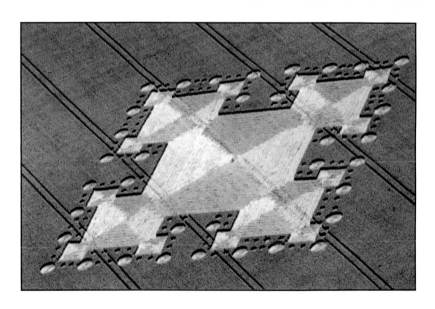

Fig. 2.13
Crop Circle formation, West Kennet, Wiltshire, 4ᵗʰ August 1999.

21

Fig. 2.14
The union of Windmill Hill and West Kennet showing a perfect fit.

The Windmill Hill crop circle represents the feminine aspect or 'socket' while the West Kennet crop circle represents the masculine aspect or 'plug'. Figure 2.14 shows the combination of these two crop circles representing the union of masculine and feminine. There are a total of **288** circles representing the 'socket'. The yellow squares and yellow circles represent the 'plug'. There are **156** yellow circles (**39 x 4**) superimposed on the **288** circles. Adding **156** to **288** brings the significant number **444**.

The harmonic number **444** is **37** times **12**. The number **12** has already been seen to hold an important place in the manifested world, also representing the passage from **1** to **2**. The number **37** is the twelfth prime number. The numbers **3** and **7** are linked to creation and represent the steps for light to be perceived in many colours by the human eye. Contained within the oneness of white light are the three primary colours and seven colours of the rainbow.

Fig. 2.15 *The Geometric Key.*
Alton Priors, Windmill Hill and West Kennet crop circles combined.

The *Geometric Key* brings both a geometric and numerical understanding of how *Pyramid Energy* works in connection with *Fractal 44*.

When *Fractal 44* is positioned on each of the four corners of the crop circle an astonishing correlation appears. An area containing **6 x 6** square units highlighted in red is formed encoding the **6 x 6 x 6** cube and a key to the fourth dimension.

In Figure 2.15, *Fractal 44* repeats itself on each corner of the original bringing a total of **188** single silver squares producing *Fractal 188*, constituting of five **4 x 4** grids, sixteen **2 x 2** grids and **44** single squares.

In three dimensions there are nine **4 x 4 x 4** hypercubes, sixty-four **2 x 2 x 2** hypercubes and finally four-hundred and forty single cubes bringing a total of **1,528** cubes.

The yellow circles form the masculine aspect of creative force, motion, frequency and voltage as a fractal element in nature. The purple circles form the feminine aspect of space and capacity ready to receive the masculine creative forces.

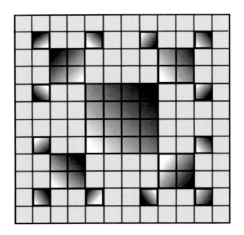

Fig. 2.16
*Fractal 44 (Alton Priors) inside the **12 x 12** grid.*

The Hebrew word 'Father'* (אב) has a *gematria value* of **3**. 'Mother' (אמ) has a *gematria value* of **41**, adding together to make **44**. The *gematria value* for 'Child' (ילד) is also **44**. *Fractal 44* encodes the Trinity of Father, Mother and Child, well known in Ancient Egypt through the personifications of Osiris, Isis and Horus.

> *"Behind the wall, the gods play, they play with numbers, of which the universe is made up."*
> **Le Corbusier**

In Figure 2.17, the yellow rectangle is the Holy Temple of Solomon. This Temple reflects the structure and motion of the universe. The accumulation point of *Zero Energy*, a **101** 'gateway' is located exactly on the most Holy Place of the Temple which is the sanctuary, shown as a green square inside the yellow rectangle. The sanctuary is a cube of edge length **20** cubits*.

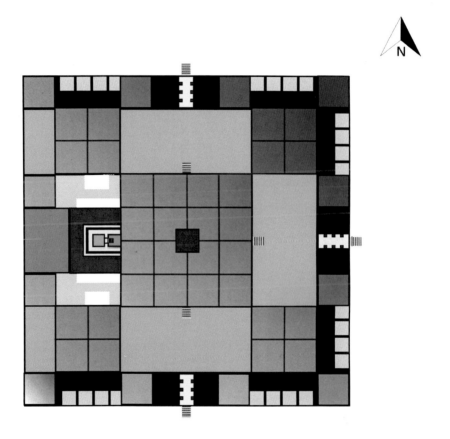

Fig. 2.17
Fractal 44 overlaid on the ground plan of the Temple of Solomon.

The Temple of Solomon from the prophetic vision of Ezekiel is five hundred cubits long and five hundred cubits wide. The Altar is shown as a red square in the centre of the **4 x 4** grid. The position of the Holy Temple is slightly different from the position of the Tabernacle suggested by *Villalpando* shown in Figure 2.8. Forty-one percent of the yellow rectangle is visible.

The illustration below shows the combination of *Fractal 44* and the ground plan of the Temple of Solomon rotated **90** degrees three times. The Holy Temple and the Altar are shown with colours. The inside and outside courtyard, the gates and the **30** chambers along the pavement are shown with red borders.

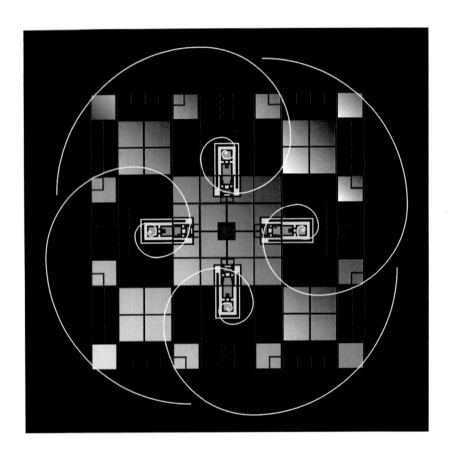

Fig. 2.18
The ground plan of the Temple of Solomon and the Golden Spirals.

The Fibonacci spiral is constructed from the green square unit representing the sanctuary. *Golden Spirals** emerge from *Zero Energy Points* showing the behaviour of the fifth element, the spiralling ether (Fig. 4.1). The Temple of Solomon is a great reminder of a connected universe, a multiple manifestation of spirals emanating from Divine Consciousness.

3. Spin Effect in the Universe • • •

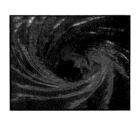

Fig. 3.1
The Divine blueprint - The Golden Spiral.

Spin effect is everywhere from the smallest particles described by scientists to planets and galaxies. In nature repeating patterns can be observed on any scale.

Historically the origin of spin was very difficult to interpret in the genesis of quantum physics. With the introduction of particle physics the spin theory was developed. Previously a physical description of the electron's structure and its spin had been a mystery. Spin is recognized to be a quantum phenomenon and its value independent from the properties of the particle yet there has been no successful physical description or any suggestion of its origin. There is still much argument as to defining the structured universe and whether matter consists of wave structures in space or particle objects with mass. In quantum theory it has been proposed that matter, substance, mass and charge do not exist, but are properties of the wave structure.

Circular motion is classified as spin or orbital motion. Spin is supposed to be the motion of an object around its center of mass. If physical objects are actually quantum waves, then spin effect is originally coming from a unified power source of energy in the universe. When two circles join to form a *Vesica Piscis* the center of each circle becomes a *Zero Energy Point*.

Everything is interconnected in the universe through energy, which means vibration and transportation. It is important to consider spin to be a quantum phenomenon and a universal mechanism observed in everything on any scale. As above, so below, universal consciousness follows the same pattern as matter in distributing energy and giving birth to the infinite grid connecting everything together through the dance of the two polarities, Yin and Yang. With this approach no physical objects can be isolated. Universal consciousness is therefore an infinite energetic grid where everything else is affected if one part of the energetic web is triggered. This is similar to a stone hitting the surface of a lake. The description of physical objects acting independently and separate from each other is not in accordance with the holographic fractal nature of space-time, which works only through vibrational energy waves.

The *Seed of Life* pattern is ever present in the geometric construction of the torus. Spin effect is caused by a power source of energy coming from the center, a *Zero Energy Point*, creating a toroidal energetic field resembling the cross section of an apple.

> "We could present spatially an atomic fact which contradicted the laws of physics, but not one which contradicted the laws of geometry."[1]
>
> **Ludwig Wittgenstein**

Fig. 3.2
Cross section of an apple.

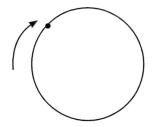

1. Single point spinning clockwise

2. Formation of the *Vesica Piscis*

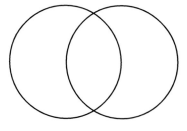

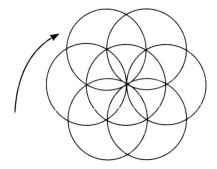

3. Rotation of the circle
Seed of Life pattern.

Fig. 3.3
Torus from a two dimensional view.

Rotation of the circle every **30°**.

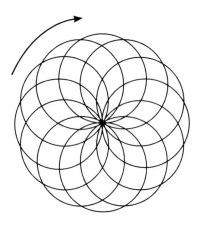

A spinning circle generates the torus on a two dimensional framework. A single point rotates around a center forming a circle. This circle then rotates around a center point outside of itself creating a series of *Vesica Piscis* forming the *Seed of Life* pattern. The circle continues to spin forming a two dimensional projection of the torus.

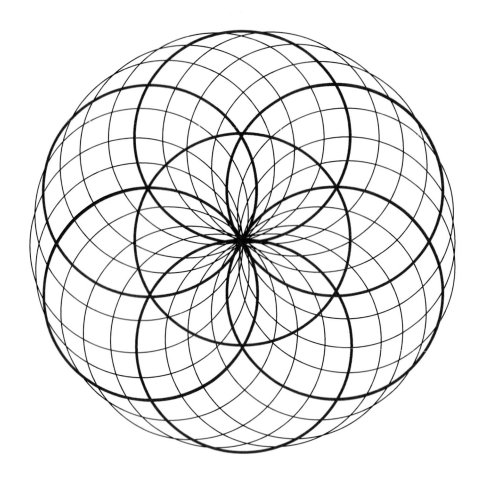

Fig. 3.4
The Seed of Life pattern highlighted in red
on the torus from a two dimensional view.

Rotation of the circle every **15°**

"*A universe of classical particles is devoid of knowledge because the universe can only be itself and not a representation of something else. If the universe was only composed of classical particles, then there would only be physical properties but no meanings. The idea that we can have information about an object without becoming that object is central to all knowledge.*"[2]
Ashish Dalela

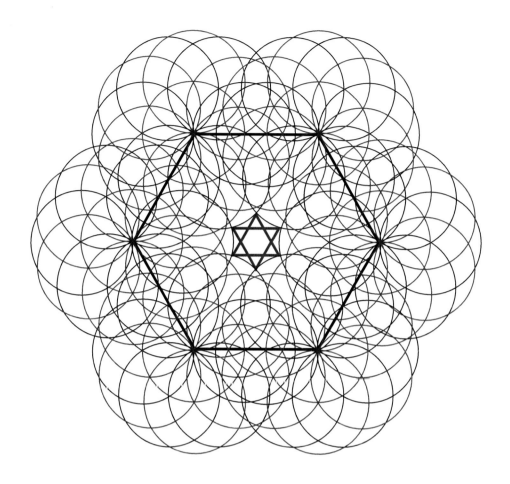

Fig. 3.5.
The spinning torus in a hexagonal shape.

There are six toroids with the *Seed of Life* pattern highlighted in red spinning around a central axis. A quantum wave can be equated to any line in the torus. The projection of a double star tetrahedron shown in blue is inscribed inside a hexagon with sides bending towards its center. The propagation of quantum waves is based on hyperbolic geometry (curved geometry). This may explain the concave sides of the Great Pyramid (Fig. 1.11).

Fig. 3.6
The seed pattern of a sunflower forming a spiraling toroidal shape*.

The sunflower shows information of spin effect from nature. The seeds are more compacted around the centre than those located at the outside edge. The geometric blueprint is a fractal expressed through an important release of energy at its centre.

Fig. 3.7
Spin effect of the sunflower.

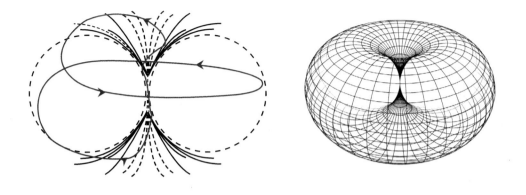

Fig. 3.8
Horn torus from a three dimensional view*.

From a three dimensional framework, the torus is a curved energetic torsion field.

The double star tetrahedron behaves in a similar fashion to the torus.

The downward pointing blue tetrahedron (female) spins anti-clockwise and the upward pointing red tetrahedron (male) spins clockwise.

Fig. 3.9
Opposing spin properties of the double star tetrahedron.

"Geometry is an 'exact' science. It leaves nothing to chance. Except for its axioms, it can prove everything it teaches. It is precise. It is definite. By it we buy and sell our land, navigate our ships upon the pathless ocean, foretell eclipses, and measure time. All science rests upon mathematics, and mathematics is first and last, geometry, whether we call its extension 'trigonometry' or 'differential calculus' or any other name. Geometry is the ultimate fact we have won out of a puzzling universe....There are no ultimate facts of which the human mind can take cognizance which are more certain, more fundamental, than the facts of geometry."[3]

Carl H. Claudy

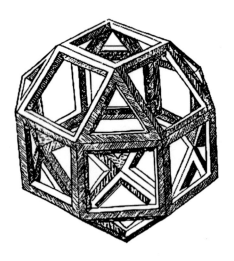

4. Yin and Yang Energy

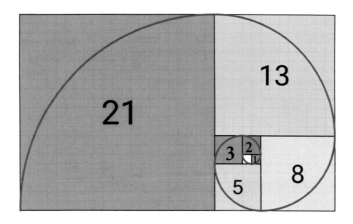

Fig. 4.1
Fibonacci Spiral forming an approximation of the Golden Spiral.

Yin and Yang energy can be observed as a Divine blueprint on any scale. The spinning spiral dance between the two polarities of Yin and Yang harmoniously celebrates the geometric nature of life.

A *Fibonacci Spiral* gradually approximates the *Golden Spiral* using quarter-circle arcs inscribed in squares of edge lengths corresponding to the Fibonacci sequence, shown here for squares with sizes of **1, 1, 2, 3, 5, 8, 13, 21**.

The *Fibonacci Spiral* or *Golden Spiral* is the path of expansion and contraction through which energy is in constant motion.

> *"Without mathematics there is no art."*
> **Luca Pacioli**

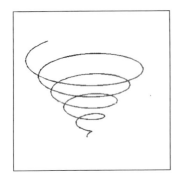

When we observe the trajectory of a spiral from the top we can see where the spiral begins but not where it ends. Another way is to view it as a constantly rotating circle expanding in a helical motion.

Fig. 4.2.
Conical Helix from a three dimensional view.

Spin effect is caused by an energetic toroidal field, each line being a quantum wave forming a huge web of points interconnected with others in the surrounding area.

Each point is not preferential and isolated but is equated to others through the principle balance of Yin and Yang. This is why universal consciousness can be geometrically interpreted through the *Flower of Life*.

A *Zero Energy Point* is located at the center of a circle from where life force manifests.

Energy wave

Zero Energy Point

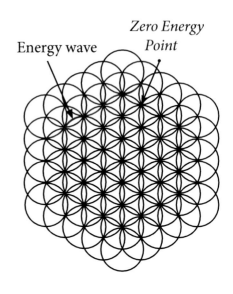

Fig. 4.3
The Flower of Life.

"The spiral in a snail's shell is the same mathematically as the spiral in the Milky Way galaxy, and it's also the same mathematically as the spirals in our DNA. It's the same ratio that you will find in very basic music that transcends cultures all over the world."

Jospeh Gordon-Levitt

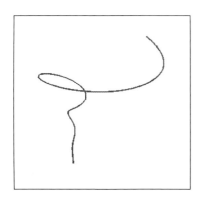

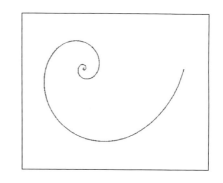

Three dimensional view   Two dimensional view

Fig. 4.4
A two and three dimensional plot from the mathematical equation of the Golden Spiral in Cartesian coordinates*.

$$r(\theta) = a\,e^{b\theta} \quad \text{with} \quad a = 1 \quad \text{and} \quad b = 0.306349 \tag{1}$$

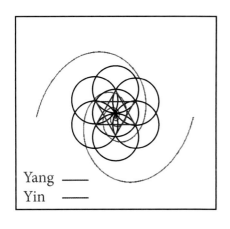

Yang ——
Yin ——

Fig. 4.5
Opposing spirals of Yin and Yang energy emanating from the center of the Seed of Life pattern.

The red triangle releases Yang energy upward and the blue triangle releases Yin energy downward. These two interlocking triangles represent the famous double star tetrahedron in three dimensions (Fig. 3.9).

The *Seed of Life* pattern *is* superimposed on the opposing *Golden Spirals* emanating from a *Zero Energy Point* in the center. Each *Zero Energy Point* on the *Flower of Life* emanates Yin and Yang *Golden Spirals*.

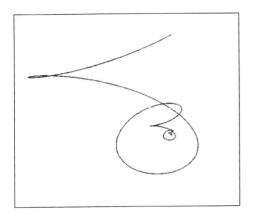

Fig. 4.6

The Golden Spiral from a three dimensional view displayed in spherical coordinates*.

The shape of this graph looks remarkably like the treble clef signature used to define the pitch of a note on a musical score.

"*Sacred Geometry charts the unfolding of number in space. It differs from mundane geometry purely in the sense that the moves and concepts involved are regarded as having symbolic value, and thus, like good music, facilitate the evolution of the soul.*"[1]

Miranda Lundy

Fig. 4.7

The side view of Figure 4.6 forming the number 8, a symbol of the universal and infinite dance.

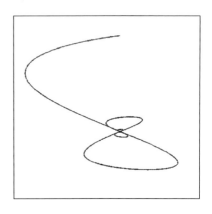

The universal dance represents 'Infinity' and the Mobius strip.

The *gematria value* for 'Love'** (אהב[2]) is **8**.

"*The atoms or elementary particles themselves are not real; they form a world of potentialities or possibilities rather than one of things or facts.*"

Werner Heisenberg

Back in two dimensions, drawn in black are the geodetic curved lines emanating from a 'point at infinity'. Like throwing a stone in a pool, blue *horocycles* ripple from this 'point at infinity'. *Horocycles* are ever expanding circular waves.

Similarly, the spiral exponentially expands and emerges from a *Zero Energy Point*. Each *Zero Energy Point* or 'point infinity' is an infinite source of potential energy connected with every other surrounding *Zero Energy Point* in the energetic grid of the *Flower of Life*.

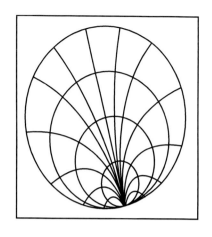

Fig. 4.8
Illustration of the horocycles.

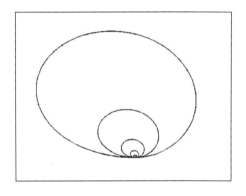

Fig. 4.9.
Top view of Figure 4.6 forming Golden Horocycles from a point at infinity.

The properties of hyperbolic geometry for a point at infinity are defined through the *Golden Horocyles* centered at this point with a factor growth of the *Golden Ratio Phi* (φ) **1.618.**

Hypercube 216 is a cube of **6 x 6 x 6** and appeared as a crop circle on Hackpen Hill on August 26th 2012, near Broad Hinton, Wiltshire.

> "The cube and the sphere are the sole working tools of creation".
>
> **Walter Russel**

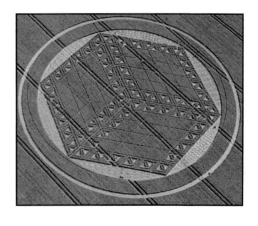

Fig. 5.1

Hackpen Hill crop circle formation.

A face of the **6 x 6 x 6** cube shown in red can be seen in the *Geometric Key* discovered through the combination of Alton Priors, Windmill Hill and West Kennet crop circles (Chapter 2).

The American philosopher and mathematician D. G. Leahy[1] made many great discoveries related to the cube **6 x 6 x 6** and found it has the uniqueness of respecting the following equation.

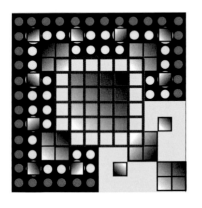

Fig. 5.2

A quadrant of the Geometric Key.

By resolving the equation, x is the edge length of the **6 x 6 x 6** cube and is equal to the square root of **10,368** which is approximately **101.823** units.

$$(x \div 6)^4 \div x^3 = 8x^3 \div x^4$$

$$X_1 = (x \div 6)^4 \div x^3$$

$$X_2 = 8x^3 \div x^4$$

$$X_1 X_2 = 1 \div 162 \ (2)$$

Surface area of a face of *Hypercube 216* :

$$x^2 = 10,368$$

Edge length x :

$$x = 72\sqrt{2} \approx 101.823$$

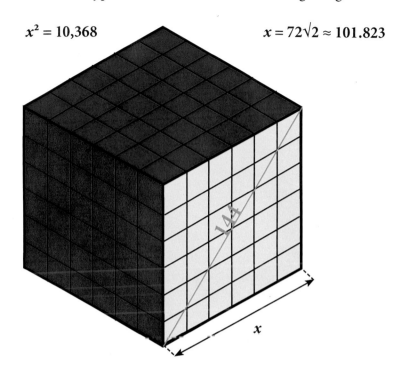

The volume* of *Hypercube 216* in four dimensions :

$$x^4 = 107,495,424$$

The diagonal line across a face is **144.**

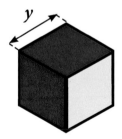

The volume of a single cube in four dimensions :

$$y^4 = (x \div 6)^4 = 82,944$$

Edge length of a single cube inside *Hypercube 216* :

$$y = x \div 6 = 12\sqrt{2}$$

Fig. 5.3
The dimensions of Hypercube 216 and a single cube.

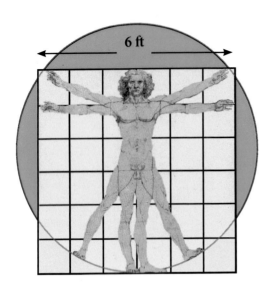

For a man six feet tall, the volume of the yellow *Hypercube 216* and the blue sphere surrounding him are both equal to **216**. On a D scale from **144 Hz**, **216** Hz is the perfect fifth A of ratio **3:2**. In the fourth dimension the volume is six power to four equal to **1296**, a double octave above E at **324** Hz of ratio **9:8**. The volume of a single cube is **1**, theoretically a Pythagorean C.

Fig. 5.4

Leonardo Da Vinci's 'Vitruvian Man'.

Hypercube 216 contains the structure of the energetic field surrounding everything from nuclear particles to planetary systems to human beings. This can be interpreted through Leonardo Da Vinci's sketch of 'Vitruvian Man'.

Hypercube 216 has an edge length of **101.823** which is close to a G# and a diagonal value of **144**, a Divine D. In the fourth dimension the volume of *Hypercube 216* is **107495424**, a Pythagorean tritone of ratio **729:512**. The volume of a single cube inside *Hypercube 216* is **82,944**, a high octave of E at **81 Hz**. The surface area of a face of *Hypercube 216* is **10368**, again another high octave of E at **81 Hz**.

The slope angle of the Great Pyramid is **51.84°**, fractally one hundredth of **5,184 Hz** which is yet again a high octave of E at **81 Hz**.

> *"The most beautiful thing we can experience is the mysterious. It is the source of all true art and science."* [2]
>
> **Einstein, Albert**

PITAGORAS

The number of circles surrounding the **6 x 6** red grid in the *Geometric Key* (Fig. 2.15) brings information about the release of energy. Thermic (heat) energy and a luminic (light) energy are quantified by the number of surrounding circles.

> " *Number is the within of all things.*"
> **Pythagoras**

Woodcut by Gaffurius

1 2 3 4 5
6 7 8 9 0

For one quadrant of the *Geometric Key* (Fig. 5.2), the **72** purple female circles represent a fractal element of luminic energy and the **39** yellow male circles represent a fractal element of thermic energy.

Therefore in each half of the *Geometric Key* there are **144** purple female circles and **78** yellow male circles. Each half of the *Geometric Key* can be viewed as a manifestation of conical etheric energy with one flowing upward and the other one downward from the center of a torus or double star tetrahedron.

The *Geometric Key* can be interpreted as an energetic toroidal field map. If we consider the *Geometric Key* as a blueprint of numerical information we are able to investigate sub atomic structure beyond any previous physical descriptions.

In the Windmill Hill crop circle there are a total of **288** purple circles representing the feminine aspect (total luminic energy). Looking at the *Geometric Key* in four dimensions, we multiply **288** by **288** giving a possible mass of **82,944** which is the numerical fractal in the volume of a single cube inside *Hypercube 216*.

When the feminine and masculine energies unite a voltage is created. In one quadrant of the *Geometric Key* the **39** male circles and the **72** female circles produce an energy frequency voltage of **2808**, as the product of **39** and **72** is **2808**.

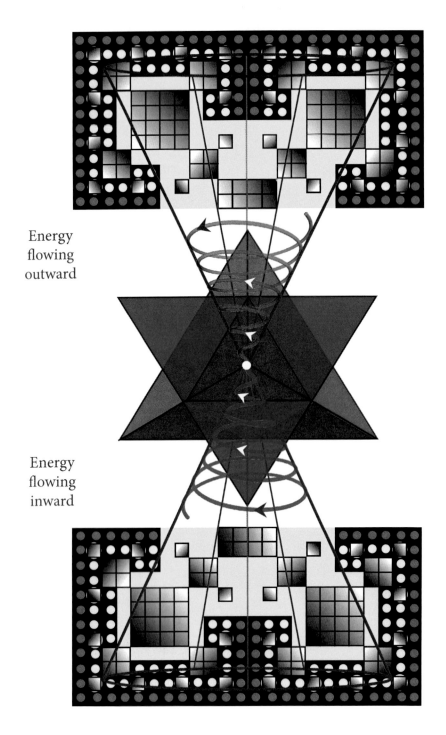

Fig. 5.5
Opposite quadrants of the Geometric Key.

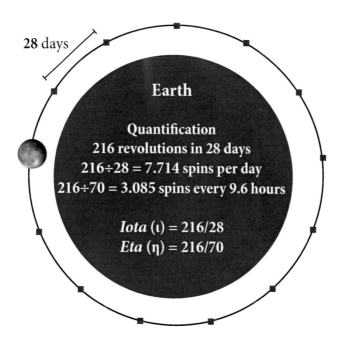

28 days

Earth

Quantification
216 revolutions in 28 days
216÷28 = 7.714 spins per day
216÷70 = 3.085 spins every 9.6 hours

Iota (ι) = 216/28
Eta (η) = 216/70

Fig. 5.6
The cycles of Hypercube 216 in a lunar calendar.

When we divide the equivalent mass of **82,944** by **2,808** we get a value approximate to the number of days in a lunar month.

$$82{,}944 \div 2{,}808 \ = \ 29.5384 \qquad\qquad (3)$$
Every full moon = **29.5306 days**

2,808 is **216** multiplied by **13** (13 moons). **216** is one tenth of the diameter of the moon in miles. Each single cube inside *Hypercube 216* has an energy frequency voltage of **13** and an equivalent mass of **384** (**384 x 216 = 82,944**). Every **28** lunar days *Hypercube 216* spins **216** times to complete a cycle. In one year it will spin **2,808** times (**28 x 13 = 364 days**).

Hypercube 216 could be regarded to stretch around the Earth and Moon. One possible interpretation is that it collapses into smaller cubes throughout the lunar cycle : *Hypercube 125* (5³), *Hypercube 64* (4³), *Hypercube 27* (3³), *Hypercube 8* (2³) and the single *Hypercube 1* during a period of **14** days (half lunar month). In a lunar calendar of **364** days, *Hypercube 216* geometrically changes every **2.8** days and completes a cycle every **28** days.

Hypercube	Energy	Equivalent mass	Cycles (days)
216	2,808	82,944	0
125	1,625	48,000	2.8
64	832	24,576	5.6
27	351	10,368	8.4
8	104	3,072	11.2
1	13	384	14
8	104	3,072	16.8
27	351	10,368	19.6
64	832	24,576	22.4
125	1625	48,000	25.2
216	2,808	82,944	28

Fig. 5.7

Equivalent mass and energy of Hypercubes during a lunar month.

The famous Rosslyn Chapel in Scotland contains some remarkable carved stone cubes protruding from pillars and arches. There are **213** cubes remaining of the original **216**. The cubes could be linked to the **216** Hebrew letters of the *Shemhampohorasch*, the forgotten or hidden Hebrew name of God.

On my visit to Rosslyn I noticed **13** different geometric designs, carved with individual symbols comprised of lines and dots, suggesting that the Knight Templar builders were aware of the science of cymatics. This puzzle could one day be deciphered to reveal more of the science of sound, light and the layout of the Divine Architecture at the core of creation.

Fig. 5.8

*Vaulting and Cubes
in Rosslyn Chapel.*

46

6. Vortex

Vortex or spiral energy connects everything in the Universe through the divine blueprint. *Chi* or *prana* life force energy emanates from *Zero Energy Points* around an axis line creating an energetic grid that resonates infinitely through all the potential points.

The symbol of the spiral has been found on many rock carvings and demonstrates a knowledge concerning the manifestation of consciousness itself. This is what connects each living being, resonating through the grid of etheric vortexes beyond the physical world.

Fig. 6.1

Spirals from Newgrange in Ireland.

The snail's shell shows the pattern of spiral energy flowing from a *Zero Energy Point*. At the birth of a snail, a *Golden Spiral* comes into existence through the mathematics of the divine blueprint. It shows the *Fibonacci Spiral* an approximation of the *Golden Ratio Phi* (φ) **1.618**.

Fig. 6.2

A snail's shell.

Ancient civilizations believed that the universe consisted of a vibrating ocean of energy called the *ether*. Their world of matter didn't exist as separate particles. Their knowledge was based on the self organization of the *ether* through the alchemy of consciousness. They were aware of standing wave interferences appearing in nature and were using devices such as stone circles to tap into the etheric energy in a practical way.

Fig. 6.3 *A petrosphere, a geometric expression of the convoluting spheres.*

The *ether* acts like a super fluid organizing itself through an arrangement of vortexes. It favours the connection of all things. The geometric patterns resulting from Sacred Geometry demonstrate how the vortexes could be organized in a structured way. On these *petrospheres* (Fig 6.3), the message from ancient civilizations seems to be that the vortexes could be organized to form the five Platonic solids in a sphere. These standing quantum wave interferences in the *ether* could be formed by using simple sound waves within the volume of the sphere. In the nineteen-fifties, Dr. Hans Jenny demonstrated through cymatics the formation of the Platonic solids within a vibrating sphere of water.

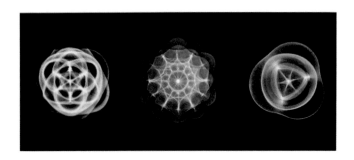

The vortexes can be arranged in twos, threes, fours and so on to form structured geometric patterns.

Fig. 6.5
The icosahedron formed.

Fig. 6.4
The double star tetrahedron formed.

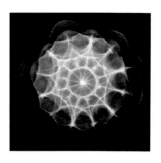

The sphere is a geometric container showing how the *ether* behaves and organizes the four fundamental interactions of Electromagnetism (expansion), Gravity (contraction), Strong and Weak Nuclear forces (cohesion of matter) from microcosm (subatomic particles) to macrocosm (celestial heavenly bodies).

The vertex positions formed are at stand-still and could be the result of a standing wave structure.

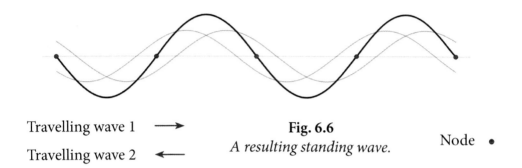

Travelling wave 1   ⟶

Travelling wave 2   ⟵

Fig. 6.6
A resulting standing wave.

Node •

A resulting standing wave is the sum of two propagating waves travelling in opposite directions. Nodes are points of no displacement. In those particular points, the *ether* vibrates with zero displacement.

Each vertex of the double star tetrahedron in three dimensions is a *Zero Energy Point* from which the dance of Yin and Yang operates and expresses a double vortex in opposition.

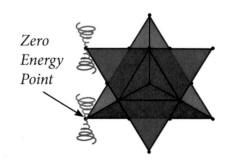

Fig. 6.7
The double star tetrahedron and the Yin and Yang Golden Spirals.

The *ether* self organizes at the quantum level forming structured geometric patterns. Universal consciousness behaves like sound waves (standing wave interference) mapping out geometric patterns of the platonic solids in a spherical volume. The two opposing propagating waves are the two Yin and Yang vortexes linked by a *Zero Energy Point*. One could say that quantum waves are sound waves and that sound waves are quantum waves.

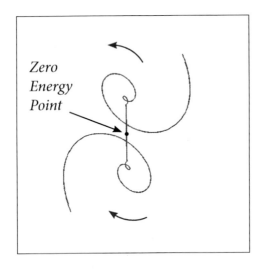

Zero Energy Point

Yang energy
Positive pole
Expansion
Anti-clockwise

Yin energy
Negative pole
Contraction
Clockwise

Fig. 6.8
Yin and Yang Golden Spirals from a three dimensional view displayed in Cartesian coordinates.*

With the principle of Yin and Yang there are two *Golden Spirals* in opposition. One is going upward, rotating anti-clockwise (Yang, positive, expansion) and the other is going downward rotating clockwise (Yin, negative, contraction). The above and following graphs have been plotted from the equation of the *Golden Spiral*. The red *Golden Spiral* is the positive pole rotating anti-clockwise Yang energy as an expansion effect. The blue *Golden Spiral* is the negative pole rotating clockwise Yin energy as a contraction effect.

Figure 6.8 is a three dimensional view of the Yin and Yang *Golden Spirals* in opposition in Cartesian coordinates. Figure 6.9 is the top view of Figure 6.8 showing the universal dance of Yin and Yang vortex energy.

> *"The world around us is a world of numbers that spell life and harmony. They are organized by the geometry of figures, all related to one another according to a sublime order, into dynamic symmetry. Glimpses into this magnificent kingdom form the basis of all our knowledge and it seems that in this domain the ancient civilizations had gone further than modern science."* [1]
>
> **Paul Jacques Grillo**

Fig. 6.9
Yin and Yang vortex energy from a two dimensional view.

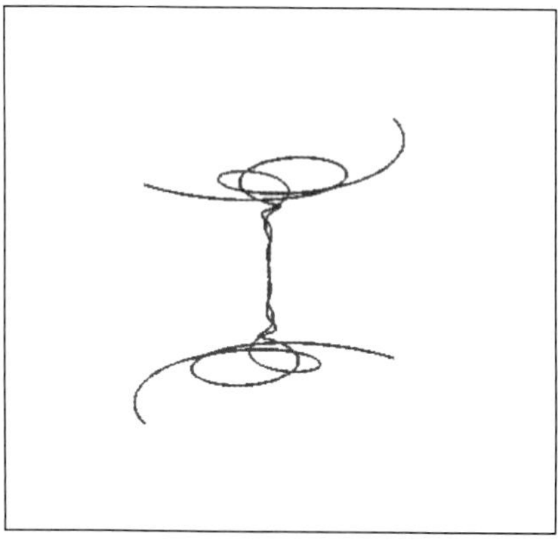

Fig. 6.10
Golden Spirals with spin effect from a three dimensional view.

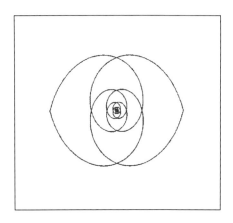

Fig. 6.11
Top view of Figure 6.4 displaying a Fibonacci sunflower pattern.

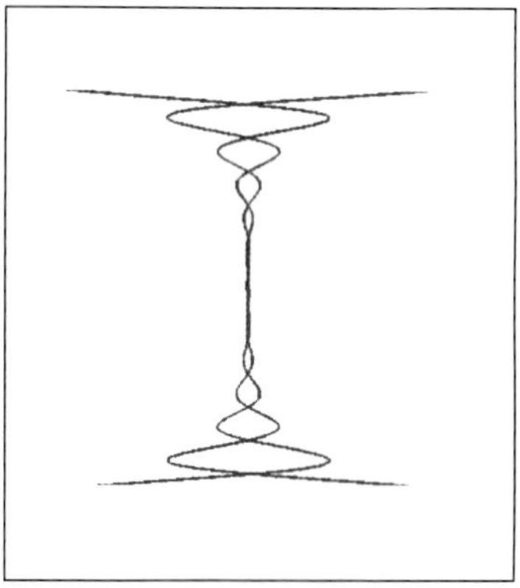

Fig. 6.12
Side view of Figure 6.5 showing opposing waves emerging from a Zero Energy Point.

"Nature hides her secrets because of her essential loftiness, but not by means of ruse. **Albert Einstein**

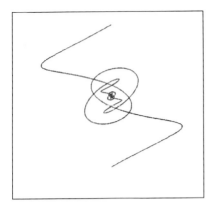

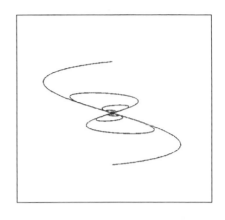

Fig. 6.13
A three dimension view of Yin and Yang Golden Spirals displayed in Spherical Coordinates*.

Fig. 6.14
'Infinity' or the number 8. Side view of Figure 6.13.

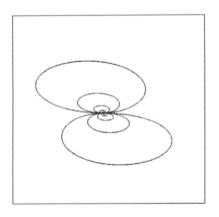

Fig. 6.15
Golden Horocycles of Yin and Yang resembling a magnetic field. Top view of Figure 6.13.

Fig. 6.16
Three dimensional side view of Figure 6.13 displaying a Yin and Yang symbol.

7. The Divine Proportion

The Divine Proportion *Phi* (φ **1.618**) is a natural manifestation at the core of universal consciousness and is related to some remarkable harmonic numbers such as **72**, **108** and **504**. Numbers are the language of consciousness creating the fundamental blocks of geometry built within the *Flower of Life*.

Universal consciousness works through standing quantum wave interferences within a sphere (Figs 6.4 and 6.5). The vortexes organize the *ether* and produce specific geometric patterns according to particular frequencies. These overlapping spheres define a convoluted Universe. Celestial bodies and fruits such as the orange or apple display a toroidal energetic field.

The sphere is directly related to the torus topologically and is the fundamental geometric shape responsible for spin with torsion effect and presence of curvature.

Fig. 7.1
The sphere.

In three dimensions, the *Flower of Life* could be interpreted as a grid of spheres overlapping each other. When a sound is produced the sphere is directly affected by vibration.

The interconnection of these spheres is expressed through the fact that they are overlapping and not separate from each other. If a sound is affecting a sphere, its neighboring spheres will also be affected.

> *"As far as the laws of mathematics refer to reality, they are not certain, and as far as they are certain, they do not refer to reality."*
> **Albert Einstein**

When a vibration is emitted from anywhere in the universe, whatever its nature, the whole interconnected grid is affected.

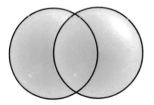

The *Vesica Piscis* represents two overlapping spheres from a three dimensional view.

Fig. 7.2
The Vesica Piscis.

The *Tripod of Life* made of three overlapping spheres is a sacred symbol and carried through the ages from ancient civilizations.

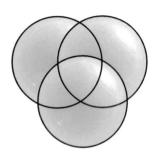

Fig 7.3
The Tripod of Life.

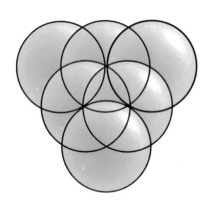

Fig 7.4
Six spheres.

A grid can be built from further overlapping spheres. The *Flower of Life* begins to appear in two dimensions.

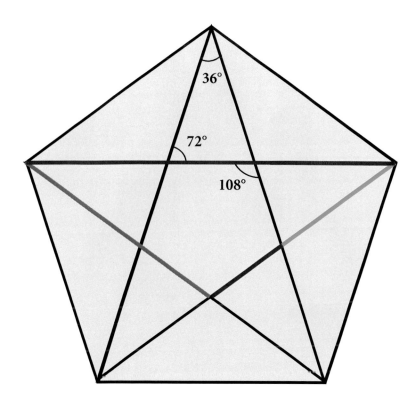

Fig. 7.5
The Pentagram.

Red ÷ green = Green ÷ blue = Blue ÷ purple = *Phi* (φ) = 1.618

The angles of the pentagram are **36**, **72** and **108**. The operation of the trigonometric functions cosine and sine on them result in numbers proportional to the *Golden Ratio Phi* (φ) or *phi* (φ) :

$$\varphi = \textit{Phi} \textbf{ (pronounced fye)} = 1.618 \tag{4}$$
$$\phi = \textit{phi} \textbf{ (pronounced fee)} = 1 \div \varphi = 0.618$$

$$\textbf{Cos } 72° = \phi \div 2 \approx 0.309 = \varepsilon = \textit{Epsilon}$$

$$\textbf{Cos } 108° = -\phi \div 2 = -\varepsilon \approx -0.309$$

$$\textbf{Cos } 36° = \varphi \div 2 \approx 0.809 = \lambda = \textit{Lambda}$$

Fig. 7.6
Natural pentagrams from top right clockwise;
star fruit, starfish, cross section of an apple and flower.

According to the German psychologist Adolf Zeising (1810–1876), the *Golden Ratio* was expressed in the growth of animal skeletons, plants and the branching patterns of their veins and nerves, as well as in the geometry of crystals. This proportion is a fundamental ratio in nature. Since 1991 several researchers have proposed connections between the *Golden Ratio* and human genome DNA.

The *Golden Ratio* is found in the pentagram, a symbol of life and growth. Through the operation of cosine, *Phi* (φ **1.618**) divided by two gives a remarkable angle of **108°**. Figure 7.5 shows the edge length relationships between the pentagram and *Phi* (φ **1.618**).

All the angles found in the pentagram are precise Pythagorean notes, **36** and **72** are both the note D. The remarkable harmonic number **108** is the musical note A on a scale from D at **72** Hz. The internal angles of the *Golden Triangle* inside the pentagram (**36, 72, 72**) produce the speed of light in miles per second when multiplied together (**186,624**).

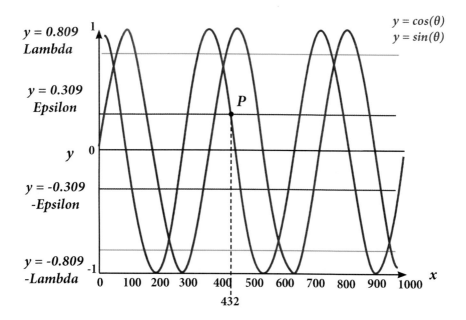

Fig. 7.7
*Harmonic numbers relating to the Divine Proportion
through the operations of cosine and sine.*

There are four equations when considering the values of both plus and minus.

18	36	54	72	108
126	144	162	198	216
234	252	288	306	324
342	378	396	414	432
468	486	504	522	558
576	594	612	648	666
684	702	738	756	774
792	828	846	864	882
918	936	954	972	

Fig. 7.8
*List of some harmonic
numbers relating to the
Divine Proportion.*

$y = \pm\,0.809 = \pm\,\textbf{Lambda}$ (λ) in turquoise.

$y = \pm\,0.309 = \pm\,\textbf{Epsilon}$ (ε) in purple.

Harmonic digit root nine numbers are at the intersection points between the equations y, cosine (blue) and sine (red). Point P shown in the graph has coordinates :

$$x = 432;\; y = \cos(432) = 0.309$$

As we have seen, **432** is a key number in both music and the Divine Blueprint.

57

Harmonics	Cos (X)	Sin (X)	Notes	Ratio	Geometry
X = 108 Hz	-ε	0.95	Perfect fifth A	3:2	Pentagon
135	-0.7	0.7	C#	15:8	Octagon
144	-λ	0.58	Divine D	1	Decagon
162	-0.95	ε	Whole tone E	9:8	Icosagon
216	-λ	-0.58	Perfect fifth A	3:2	
234	-0.58	-λ	13th Harmonic	13:8	
252	-ε	-0.95	C	7:4	
288	ε	-0.95	D	1	
306	0.58	-λ	E^b	17:16	
360	1	0	F#	5:4	Circle Square
486	-0.58	λ	Major sixth B	27:16	
666	0.58	-λ	37th Harmonic	37:32	
702	0.95	-ε	39th Harmonic	39:32	

Fig. 7.9

Musical notes, ratios and regular polygons
from some of the harmonic numbers in Figure 7.8.

Any number with digits adding up to **9** when divided by **9** shows its harmonic position in a musical system from D at **9** Hz. When **666 is** divided by **9** the result is the 74th harmonic from D at **9** Hz. Certain key harmonic number are not produced by the program. Other numbers connected with the regular polygons do not appear.

We do see however **162** (18th harmonic), the interior angle of a twenty sided icosagon. The decagon, octagon and the circle or square also equate to musical notes through their interior angles and are respectively a Divine D at **144** Hz, a C# at **135** Hz and F# at **180** Hz or **90** Hz.

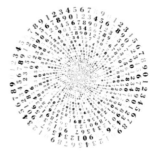

" *Number rules the universe.*" **Pythagoras**

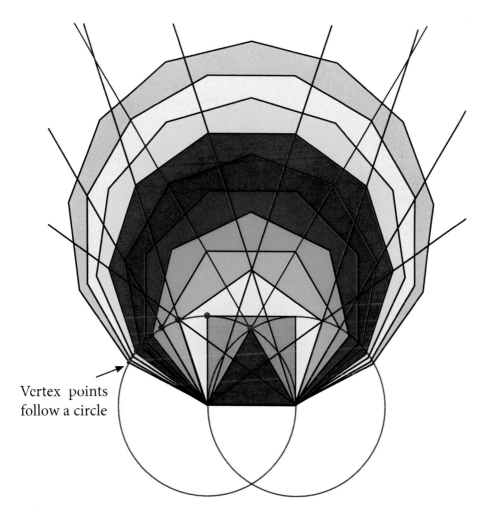

Vertex points follow a circle

Fig. 7.10
The Vesica Piscis generating the regular polygons.

Regular polygons created by the *Vesica Piscis* all share an edge length of the radius of the circle. Red dots mark the corners (vertexes) of each polygon following the path of a circle.

Geometry and musical notes emanate from the center of the *Vesica Piscis*.

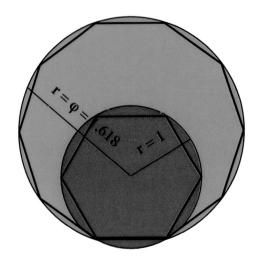

The blue circle surrounding the decagon has a radius equal to the *Golden Ratio Phi* (φ) and the red circle surrounding the hexagon has a radius equal to **1**.

Fig. 7.11
The hexagon and decagon.

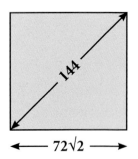

Fig. 7.12
A face of Hypercube 216.

For a face of *Hypercube 216* the diagonal is equal to **144**, a Divine D. The edge length of **72√2** (**101.823**) is close to a G#.

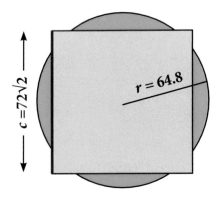

Fig. 7.13
A face of Hypercube 216 squaring the circle*.

Perimeter of P(square) = **4c**
Perimeter of P(circle) = **2πr**
P(square) = P(circle) = **288√2**

The edge length of *Hypercube 216* corresponds to G# and the perimeter of the blue circle is also a G#. Changing notes in music is therefore equivalent to changing shapes in geometry.

* See Appendix C

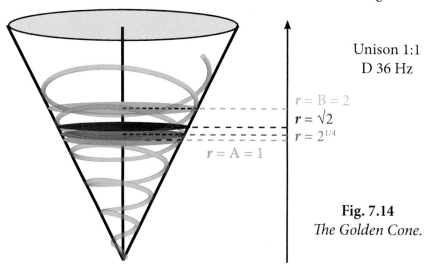

Radius of the circle ascending

Unison 1:1
D 36 Hz

$r = B = 2$
$r = \sqrt{2}$
$r = 2^{1/4}$

$r = A = 1$

Fig. 7.14
The Golden Cone.

At certain distances along the axis of the cone, the radii of cross sections from the *Golden Cone* produces remarkable musical notes when *Theta* (θ) is calculated in equation (5).

$$r(\theta) = e^{b\theta} \quad \text{with} \quad \theta \text{ (radian)} = \ln(r) \div b \quad \text{and} \quad b = 0.306349 \tag{5}$$

$$\theta \text{ (degrees)} = \theta \text{ (radian)} \times (180 \div \pi)$$

Figure 7.15 lists the values of *Theta* (θ) for some values of radius *r*.

Parameters	Blue circle	Orange circle	Purple circle	Green circle
Radius *r*	1	$2^{1/4}$	$\sqrt{2}$	2
θ **(rad)**	0	0.565	1.13	2.26
θ **(deg)**	0	32.4	64.8	129.6
Music		C	C	C
θ **(deg)** π	0	101.817	203.64	407.28
Music		G#	G#	G#

Fig. 7.15
Musical notes produced by the Golden Cone.

61

In Figure 7.14, the blue circle has a radius equal to **1** (unison **1:1**) and the green circle has a radius equal to **2** (octave **2:1**) after one complete revolution of the *Golden Spiral*. The purple circle has a radius √2 corresponding to the tritone. Further musical notes can be obtained when *Theta* (θ) is multiplied by *Pi* (π). A circle of radius *r* equal to $2^{1/4}$ produces the angle **101.817** which is close to a G# and also remarkably close to the edge length of *Hypercube 216*. A circle of radius *r* equal to √2 produces an angle of **203.64** close to a G#. A circle of radius *r* equal to **2** produces an angle of **407.28** (also close to a G#). *Hypercube 216* is intrinsically connected with the behavior of the *Golden Spiral* in nature.

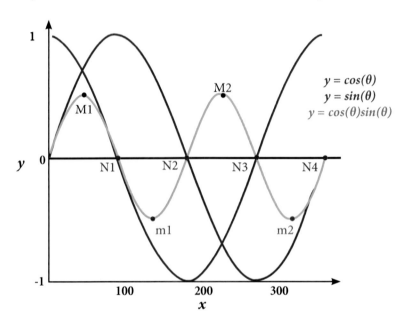

Fig. 7.16
A two dimensional graph of standing wave interferences.

The points *M* and *m* mark the peaks whilst the *N* points mark intersections. The x-axis on the green line is plotted from the equation of standing wave interferences. These points correspond to the radii of a *Golden Spiral* in motion describing an expanding circle every **45** degrees, from equation (5). At every 45 degrees the radius increases by a multiple factor of the square root of *Phi* (√φ = **1.273**) or the height of the Great Pyramid as shown in Figure 1.14.

Pt	N1	M1	N2	m1	N3	M2	N4	m2	N5
θ (°)	0	45°	90°	135°	180°	225°	270°	315°	360°
Mus		F#	F#	C#	F#	25th	C#	35th	F#
r	1	$\sqrt{\varphi}$	φ	$\varphi^{3/2}$	φ^2	$\varphi^{5/2}$	φ^3	$\varphi^{7/2}$	φ^4
v	0	0.5	0	-0.5	0	0.5	0	-0.5	0
θ π	0	141.4	282.8	424.1	565.5	706.9	848.2	989.6	1,131
Mus		63rd	63rd	47th	63rd	39th	47th	55th	63rd

Fig. 7.17

Musical notes produced by standing wave interferences.

First row : Points *M*, *N* and *m* from Figure 7.16.

Second row : *Theta* (θ) from equation (5).

Third row : Musical notes from the second row.

Fourth row : Radii from equation (5).

Fifth row : Values read on y-axis in Figure 7.16.

Sixth row : Second row *Theta* (θ) multiplied by *Pi* (π).

Seventh row : Musical notes from the sixth row.

When *Theta* (θ) is equal to **144** degrees, the interval ratio of the corresponding musical note is **11:7**, the Great Pyramid base leg to height ratio. The equivalent radius of the *Golden Spiral* is **2.16**.

When the radius *r* from a cross section of the *Golden Spiral* is equal to **3.168**, *gematria value* for 'Lord Jesus Christ'* (Κυριος ιησους χριστος[1]), the equivalent angle *Theta* (θ) is approximately equal to **216°** a perfect fifth A.

> "Like God, the Divine proportion is always similar to itself."
>
> **Lucas Pacioli**

8. The Etheric Particle

The reigning theory of particle physics is the Standard Model which describes the basic building blocks of matter and how they interact. The theory was developed in the early 1970's and has become established as a well tested theory. In the Standard Model scientists are still searching for a missing particle to unify the four fundamental interactions; gravity, electromagnetism, strong and weak nuclear forces.

1. Gravity is a force attracting a body towards its orbital center.
2. Electromagnetism (EM) is a release of energy radiating in all directions from any matter. This includes radio waves, microwaves, X-rays and Gamma rays. Sunlight is a form of electromagnetism.
3. Strong nuclear forces are responsible for binding together the fundamental particles of matter to form larger particles.
4. Weak nuclear forces are responsible for decay and deconstruction. Radioactive decay converts hydrogen into helium and powers the sun in the Standard Model.

These four forces are generated by the *Etheric Particle* through the four *Zero Energy Points* of *Fractal 44*, represented by the base of a pyramid. The Standard Model fails to acknowledge this fifth force that brings order to the universe as it would violate the Second Law of Thermodynamics, which states there is a natural tendency towards disorder or maximum entropy.

The *Etheric Particle* embodies the geometric code of a fifth force operating outside the physical dimension. Prior to the establishment of the Standard Model there was much debate about the *ether* and spin effect.

The fifth element operates throughout all matter but remains undetectable by scientific measurement.

This chapter will deal with the encodement of the *Etheric Particle* as referred by the Bible in the description of the *New Jerusalem*.

The Great Pyramid encodes the architecture of the *Etheric Particle* and reflects the relative sizes of the Earth and Moon.

On a two dimensional framework twelve moons are positioned around the Earth in four groups of three. Each moon has a section angle of almost **26** degrees **(360÷14)**. A red circle divided into **28** points runs through the center of each moon. These points lie either in the center or on the edges of the moons. The *Etheric Particle* is inscribed inside a **12** sided dodecagon shown in Figure 8.1. Earth's diameter is equal to **22** and the diameter of each moon is equal to **6**.

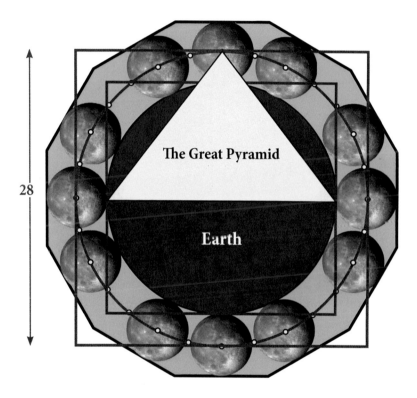

Fig. 8.1
The Etheric Particle.

> "*Etheronic energy is the emanation from the spirit force through the active force of that which makes for matter being held in its positive position, or in its space of activity. Hence thought as a body, whether of animal or plant, is shown as of plant receiving in its freshness of vigour influences that come from or through the etheronic energy in its activity upon the body, in the expression or upon the plant as in its expression. Hence things that are equal to the same thing are equal to each other.*"
>
> **Edgar Cayce**

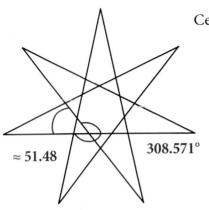

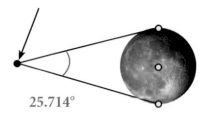

Center of the *Etheric Particle*

≈ 51.48

308.571°

25.714°

2,160 ÷ 7 = 308.571°

Eta (η) = 216 ÷ 70 = 3.085

2,160 Moon's diameter in miles

Fig. 8.2
The numerical key
of the 7-pointed star.

The factor *Eta* (η) **3.085 (216÷70)** is the number of spins of *Hypercube 216* every **9.6** hours in a lunar day (Fig 5.6). Twelve moon angle sections of **25.714** degrees make a total of **308.571** degrees. This number appears in the geometry of the seven pointed star shown in Figure 8.2 linking the *Etheric Particle* with *Hypercube 216*. **308.571** is also known as the *Sacred Angle* of **360** minus a seventh of **360**.

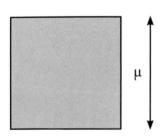

μ

Edge length of the square *Mu* (μ) :

$$\sqrt{(72\sqrt{2})} = 6 \times 2^{1/4} \approx 7.135 \approx \sqrt{51}$$

$$\mu \approx 153 \times (0.216)^2$$

Fig. 8.3
A Numerical Key of Hypercube 216.

The square root of the edge length of *Hypercube 216* is $\sqrt{(72\sqrt{2})}$, which can also be written as **6 x 2¹ᐟ⁴**, another numerical key *Mu* (μ). Geometrically it can be seen as the length of two sides of a square of area* **36√2**. This key can be calculated with the numbers **153** and **216**.

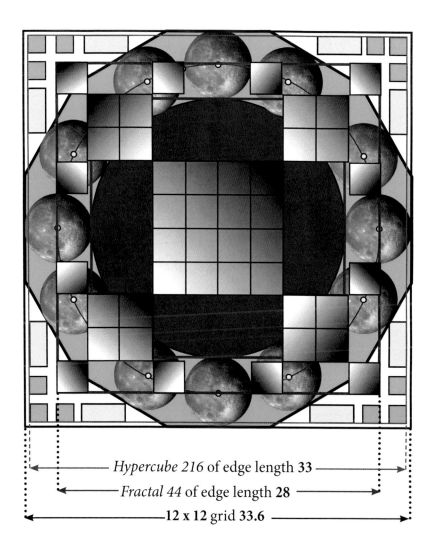

Hypercube *216* of edge length **33**
Fractal 44 of edge length **28**
12 x 12 grid **33.6**

Fig. 8.4
The correlation between the Etheric Particle and Fractal 44.

There are **12** moons arranged in **12** squares around the perimeter. If the correlation is mathematically correct, the centre of Earth would be the center of the Zodiacal sphere. It supports the ancient geocentric model of the universe with Earth at the centre. In Aristotle and Ptolemy's time the Sun, Moon and stars all circled the Earth. The heliocentric model of Copernicus, Galileo and Kepler gradually superseded the geocentric model from the late sixteenth century onwards.

Another astonishing geometric correlation appears by superimposing the **12 x 12** grid on the *Etheric Particle*. The black outline around the *Etheric Particle* meets the edges of the **12** sided dodecagon. Yellow rectangles and green squares in the corners come from building upon *Fractal 44* (Fig. 2.3). *Fractal 44* represents the physical world of tangible matter while etheric activity operates outside of the red square of edge length **28**.

*"And the city lieth four square, and the length is as large as the breadth; and he measured the city with the reed **12,000** furlongs. The length and the breadth, and the height of it are equal."*

In the book of Revelations 21:16, it suggests that the city of the *New Jerusalem* has an edge length equal to a cube with a volume of **12,000** furlongs.
In feet, **12,000** furlongs is equal to **12,000** multiplied by **660** resulting in **7,920,000** feet. The cube root of this number is approximately **199.333** feet. The Bible also states that the outside wall of the *New Jerusalem* is separated from the inside wall by an area of **144** cubits or **324** square feet which brings an edge length value of approximately **235.333** feet. This may seem a small measurement for a city but could represent just an inner section.

In the Bible the number **616** can be taken as a variant of the Number of the Beast **666** in Revelation 13:18. The number **308** is the integer part of the *Sacred Angle* **308.571** and multiplied by **2** makes **616**. The number **666** is encoded in the outside wall of the *New Jerusalem* by doubling the diagonal of a face of a cube of edge length **235.45**.

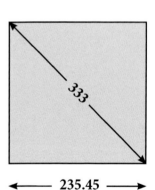

← 235.45 →

Fig. 8.5
The outside wall of the New Jerusalem in feet.

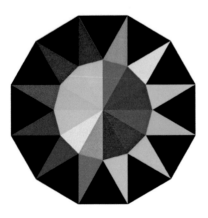

The table below compares numerical information from the *Etheric Particle* on different scales.

Edge length	Edge A	B (units) = A x *Eta* (η)	C (feet) = A x *Mu* (μ)	D (miles) = A x 360
Square unit	2.8	8.64	19.978	1,008
Moon's diam	6	18.514	42.811	2,160
Earth's diam	22	67.885	156.975	7,920
Fractal 44 Inside Wall	28	86.4	199.786	10,080
Hypercube 216 Outside Wall	32.998	101.823	235.45	11,879.28
12 x 12 grid	33.6	103.68	239.744	12,096
Cornerstone 666	51.84	160	370	18,667.9

Fig. 8.6
Data extrapolated from the Etheric Particle model.

- Edge length *A* column is the reference column.
- Edge length *B* column comes from the dimensions of *Hypercube 216* in units.
- Edge length *C* column is produced from Edge *A* multiplied by the numerical key *Mu* (μ) and represents values in feet.
- Edge length *D* column is produced from Edge *A* multiplied by **360** and represents values in miles.

On scale *C*, the edge length of *Fractal 44* is approximately equal to the edge length of the inside wall of the *New Jerusalem* **199.333** feet and the edge length of *Hypercube 216* is approximately equal to **235.333** feet.

On scale *B*, the number of revolutions in **2** lunar days is almost the difference between the edge length of *Hypercube 216* and *Fractal 44* suggesting that the architecture of the *Etheric Particle* encodes the quantification of its spin dynamics.

$$101.823 - 86.4 = 15.423 = 7.711 \times 2 \approx \textit{Iota} (\iota) (216 \div 28) \times 2 \qquad (6)$$

The edge length of the walls of the *New Jerusalem* can be approximately calculated with the factor *Psi* (Ψ) (10,368÷3,168 ≈ 3.28) the surface area of a face of *Hypercube 216* being **10,368** and the *gematria value* for 'Lord Jesus Christ' being **3,168**. These edge lengths can also be calculated approximately with the *Golden Ratio Phi* (φ **1.618**) and *phi* (φ **0.618**).

The red area covered by *Fractal 44* has an edge length equal to **199.63636** feet (**61** x *Psi* Ψ) and is approximately equal to **18** φ^5 feet or the following equation $\varphi^{11} - \phi^{11} + 2 \div \pi$ with $\pi = 22 \div 7$.

The inverse *psi* (ψ = 1÷Ψ) is equal to **0.3055**, an approximate value of one foot in meters.

The circumference of the *Christ Circle* is approximately **1,480** (10,368÷7). On scale *B* from Figure 8.5, the radius of the *Christ Circle* is equal to **235.63636** which is also the edge length of the outside wall of the *New Jerusalem* in feet.

Perimeter 10,368÷7 ≈ 1,481

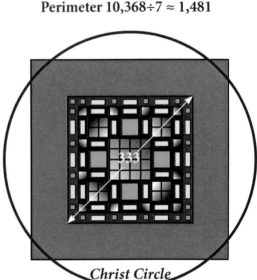

Edge length of orange square :
370 feet
Edge length of red square :
199.63636 feet
Edge length of purple square :
235.63636 feet
Double diagonal across
the purple and red squares :
666 feet

Fig. 8.7
The Cornerstone 666.

The purple area covered by the **12 x 12** grid has an edge length to **235.63636** feet (**72** x *Psi* Ψ) and is approximately equal to **18** $(2 + \varphi^5)$ feet.

The *gematria value* for 'Christ'* (χριστος[1]) is **1,480**.

The *gematria value* for 'Pharez'* (רפץ the Breaker[2]) is **370**.

Fig. 8.8
*Correlation between the Cornerstone **666** and the Geometric Key.*

The *Tesseract* is the term for a fourth dimensional cube or a larger cube containing a smaller cube. The orange cube of edge length **370** feet contains the *New Jerusalem* purple cube of edge length **235.63636** feet.

Figure 8.8 shows the correlation between the *Geometric Key* (Fig 2.15) and the *Cornerstone* **666** (Fig 8.7). The *Christ Circle* is projected in red squaring the orange square and almost touching the edges of the *Geometric Key*.

> *"The construction of the physical and moral world alike is based on eternal numbers."*   **St Augustine**

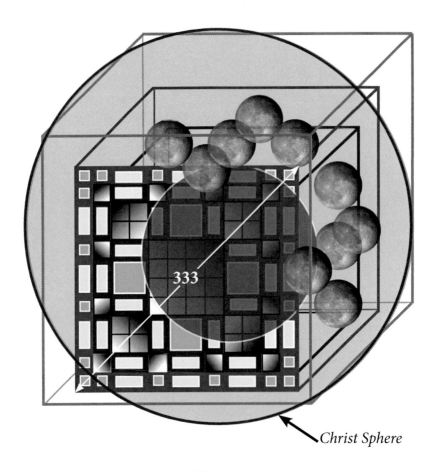

333

Christ Sphere

Fig. 8.9
*A three dimensional view of the Etheric Particle including
the Cornerstone **666** within the Christ Sphere.*

From the *Christ Circle* comes the *Christ Sphere* with a radius equal to **235.63636** feet, the edge length of *Hypercube 216* and the outside wall of the *New Jerusalem*.

There are five moons positioned on each face of the cube making a total of **30** moons around the Earth. The red and purple cubes are respectively the inside and outside wall of the *New Jerusalem*. The orange cube is defining the fourth dimension.

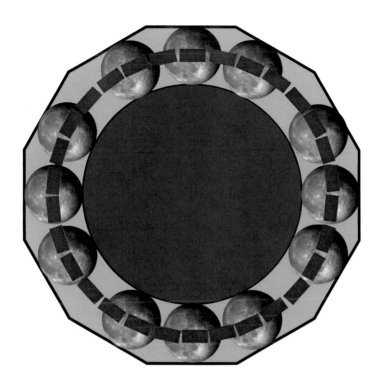

▬ Position of Sarsen stones at Stonehenge

Fig. 8.10
Correlation between Stonehenge and the Etheric Particle.

There are **30** upright stones forming in the Sarsen circle at Stonehenge mirroring the **30** moons of the *Etheric Particle* from a three dimensional view (Fig. 8.9).

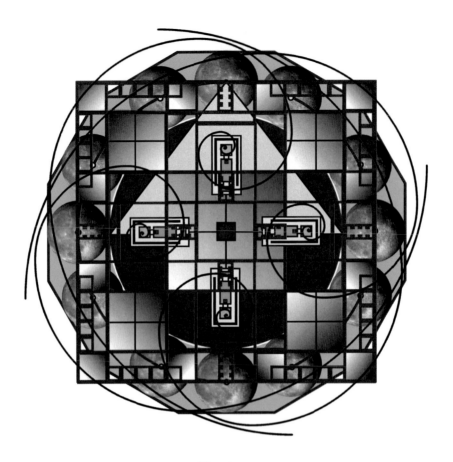

Fig. 8.11
*A combination of the ground plan of the Temple of Solomon,
the Great Pyramid and Fractal 44.*

Four *Golden Spirals* emanate from *Zero Energy Points* positioned in the four sanctuaries of the Temple of Solomon. These spirals represent the fifth force or *ether* coming from a pyramid base amplifying the natural order. The thirty chambers around the inside of the outer courtyard of the Temple of Solomon and the thirty chambers inside the Holy Temple* may relate to the **30** moons of the *Etheric Particle* from a three dimensional view.

Now let's examine some significant astronomical distances and the sizes of the Sun, Moon and Earth. These distances hold harmonic numbers found in the geometrical construct and the dynamic spin of the *Etheric Particle* and *Hypercube 216*.

Some of these numbers are also encoded in the architecture of Glastonbury Abbey in relation to the light year, the distance that light travels in one year.

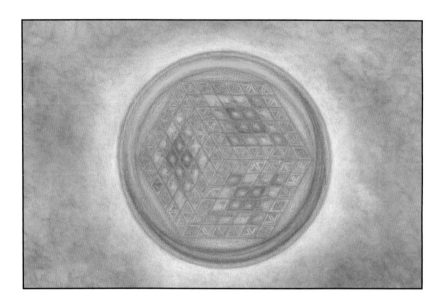

Fig. 9.1
Artistic expression of Hackpen Hill crop circle (Fig 5.1).

There is perfect harmony in our solar system based around the harmonic numbers **27, 54, 108, 216, 432, 864, 1,728,** and so on. They are part of the fundamental blocks of cosmic architecture. For e.g., the distance from the Sun to Earth is **108** times the Sun's diameter and the distance from Earth to the Moon is **108** lunar diameters.

The Sun's diameter is **864,000** miles, approximately **108** times the Earth's diameter or **400** lunar diameters.

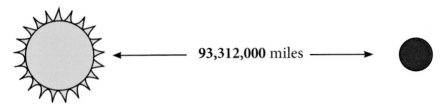

108 solar diameters = 108 x 864,000 = 18,000 x 5,184

Fig. 9.2
Earth's distance from the Sun.

108 lunar diameters = 108 x 2,160 = 45 x 5,184

Fig. 9.3
Moon's distance from the Earth.

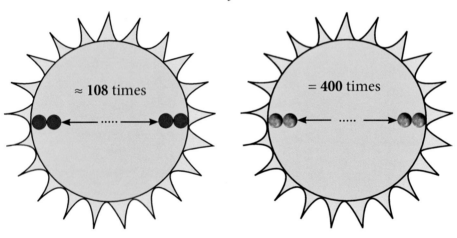

Fig. 9.4	**Fig. 9.5**
The Sun and Earth's diameter.	*The Sun and Moon's diameter.*

7,920 x 108 ≈ 864,000 miles   **2,160 x 400 = 864,000 miles**

> *"The cosmos is full beyond measure of elegant truths; of exquisite interrelationships; of the awesome machinery of nature."*
> **Carl Sagan**

The circle representing Earth's diameter of **7,920** miles is inscribed inside a square of perimeter **31,680** miles, with **3,168** being the *gematria value* for 'Lord Jesus Christ'. The volume *V* of the *Christ Sphere* of the *Etheric Particle* is calculated from the perimeter of this square shown in equation (7). The value of *Pi* (π) is taken as **3.144605***.

$$V = (4 \div 3)\,\pi\,(235.45)^3 \approx 54{,}726{,}918 \text{ ft}^3 \tag{7}$$
$$V \approx 1{,}728 \times 31{,}680 \approx 660 \times 82{,}944 = 54{,}743{,}040 \text{ ft}^3$$

The volume *V* is approximately **1,728** multiplied by **31,680** or **660** multiplied by the volume of a cube inside *Hypercube 216* in four dimensions **82,944** (Fig 5.3). **660** ft is defined as a furlong in the international system of measurement.

Perimeter $P = 7{,}920 \times 4 = 31{,}680$ miles.

Fig. 9.6
Earth and the Christ Sphere.

The volume of eight **Christ Spheres V8** has a radius approximately equal to half the perimeter of the outside wall of the *New Jerusalem* **470.9** feet.

$$V8 = 8 \times V \approx 8 \times 54{,}726{,}918 = 437{,}815{,}344 \tag{8}$$
$$\approx (4 \div 3)\,\pi\,(470.9)^3$$
$$\approx 5{,}280 \times 82{,}944 = 437{,}944{,}320$$

The volume **V8** is approximately equal to **5,280** multiplied by the volume of a cube in four dimensions **82,944**. In the international system of measurement, **5280** ft is defined as a mile.

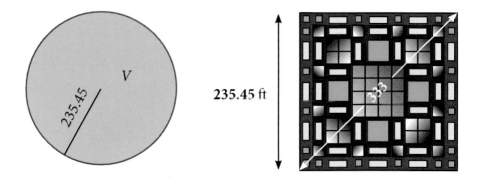

In Figure 8.6 on scale *C* the edge length of *Hypercube 216* or the outside wall of the *New Jerusalem* is **235.45** ft and corresponds to the radius of a *Christ Sphere*. Eight spheres together share the same volume as a sphere of radius **470.9** ft, diameter of a *Christ Sphere* and the half perimeter of the outside wall.

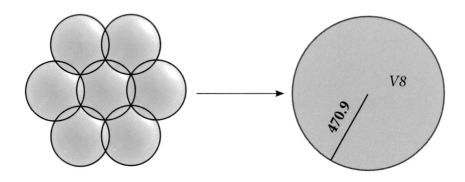

Fig. 9.7
*Relationships between the dimensions of Hypercube 216
or the New Jerusalem and the Christ Sphere.*

8 Spheres (The 8th sphere is hidden behind the central sphere).

The number **8** plays an important role at the core of creation. The *Seed of Life* pattern is the foundation from which the *Egg of Life* takes form. This pattern is made of seven interlocking circles forming the cellular structure of the third embryonic division. The first cell divides into two cells, four cells and finally into eight cells.

Same as the formation of *Christ Spheres*; As above, so below.

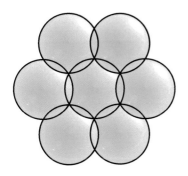 

Fig. 9.8
The process of manifestation.

A light year is defined as a unit of astronomical distance equivalent to the distance that light travels in one year. Light is a geometric expression based upon the dimensions of *Hypercube 216*. The speed of light in a vacuum is **186,624** miles per second (**432** squared) or **18** multiplied by **10,368**. The harmonic number **10,368** is the surface area of a face of *Hypercube 216* (Fig 5.3).

A solar year is **365** days. In a day, there are **86,400 (24 x 3,600)** seconds. The following equation shows the number of miles in a light year.

$$365 \text{ x } 86,400 \text{ x } 186,624 = 5,885,374,464,000 \qquad (9)$$
$$= 107,495,424 \text{ x } 54,750$$
$$\approx 107,495,424 \text{ x } 740 \text{ x } 74$$

The result is the volume of *Hypercube 216* in four dimensions **107,495,424** multiplied by **54,750** (**740** multiplied by **74**).

In the early part of the twentieth century, archaeologist Frederick Bligh Bond discovered Glastonbury Abbey was constructed over a regular grid of squares of **74 ft** or **888** inches[1].

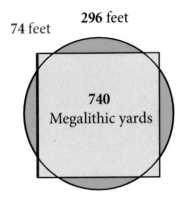

Fig. 9.9

A square unit in the ground plan of Glastonbury Abbey.

The circumference of the green circle is **296**, the *gematria value* for 'Water from the rock'* (רְמִים מסלע[2]).

A square unit in the ground plan of Glastonbury Abbey has a side of **74** feet and an area of **740** megalithic yards. A megalithic yard is a unit of measurement close to **2.72** feet (**0.83** meters) and was used in the construction of megalithic structures.

The mathematical construct of light is encoded within the geometry of *Hypercube 216* and has as a foundation the number **37**, which is a tenth of **370 ft** (the edge length of the *Cornerstone* **666** in the *Geometric Key*) bridging the third and fourth dimensions (Figs 8.7 and 8.8). The number **74** is the *gematria value* for the Hebrew word 'Foundation'* (יסד[3]).

Many numerical keys relating to the fourth dimension can be found in the cosmic architecture of megalithic structures.

Another good example is the Sun to galactic center distance **D**, reckoned to be **25,000** light years. The divisors of distance **D** in miles can be expressed in some of the following ways.

$$D = 25{,}000 \times 740 \times 74 \times 107{,}495{,}424 = 370^2 \times 10^4 \times 107{,}495{,}424 \tag{10}$$

$$= 370^2 \times 12{,}960{,}000 \times 82{,}944 = 147{,}161{,}235{,}456{,}000{,}000$$

Dropping the zeros from the total number of miles and adding each group of three digits, the result is a number of root **9**.

$$147 + 161 + 235 + 456 = 999 \tag{10}$$

10. The Universal Architecture

The *universal architecture* embodies the geometry of light, the *Cornerstone* **666** (Fig 8.7), the *Etheric Particle* (Fig 8.9), *Vitruvian Man* (Fig 5.4) and the planetary system (Figs 9.2 and 9.3). This geometric correlation brings a deeper awareness of an interconnected universe.

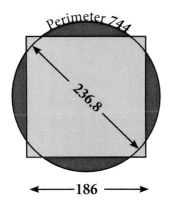

Fig. 10.1
Geometry of Light, Key A.
Squaring the circle.

The golden square with an edge length equal of **186** is related to the speed of light (**186,624** miles per seconds). The perimeter is equal to **744** and squares the circle of diameter **236.8**. The *gematria value* for 'Two Great Lights'* (המאודת הגדלים[1]) in Hebrew is **744**.

The *gematria value* for 'Jesus Christ'* (ιησουσ χριστος[2]) is **2,368** which is the sum of **888**, the *gematria value* for 'Jesus'* (ιησουσ[3]) and **1,480** for 'Christ'* (χριστος[4]) in the Greek biblical scriptures.

The perimeter of the *Christ Sphere* is **1,480** and is inscribed inside a blue square of edge length **470.9** representing half the perimeter of the outside wall of the *New Jerusalem* in feet. The turquoise circle surrounding this square has a diameter of **666** and a perimeter *P* equal to **1480√2**, approximately **2093**.

The dimensions of the *universal architecture* are calculated with *Pi* (π) equal to **3.1426968****.

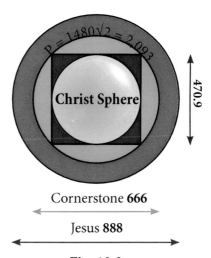

Cornerstone **666**

Jesus **888**

Fig. 10.2
Cornerstone 666 in the Etheric Particle, Key B.

In the biblical scriptures Ezekiel described a gifted land (the holy oblation) of **25,000** reeds, representing the universe as a cube container of edge length **25,000** units (*Ezekiel Chapters* 40-48). One twelfth of the edge length of this square is equal to approximately **2093**.

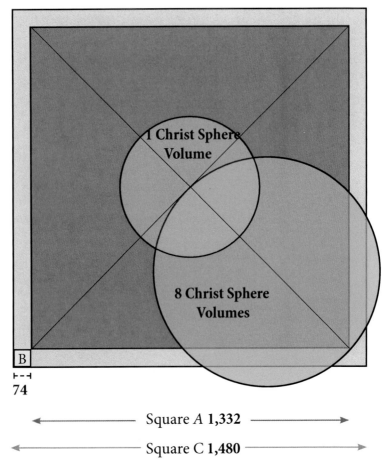

Fig. 10.3
The eight Christ Spheres, Key C.

Half of the diagonal of the purple square *A* is **941.8** ft, also the perimeter of the outside wall of the *New Jerusalem* and the diameter of a sphere of a volume *V8* equivalent to the total volume of **8** *Christ Spheres* (Fig 9.6). Figure 10.3 shows the geometric construction of square *C* if a square unit *B* from the ground plan of Glastonbury Abbey (Fig 9.8) is placed on each corner of square *A*.

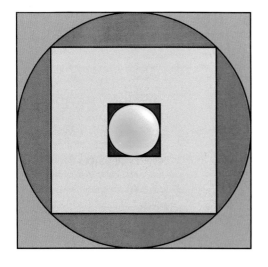

Fig. 10.4
One square unit of the
***12 x 12** grid of the*
gifted land, Key D.

The next step in the geometric construction is to draw a circle around square *C*. Square *D* with an edge length approximately **2,093** is constructed around the orange circle. Square *D* is one square unit of a **12 x 12** grid representing the gifted land described by Ezekiel.

⟵ Square C **1,480** ⟶

⟵——— Square D **2,093** ———⟶

Four purple circles *E* of diameter **148** are placed on each corner of square *C* creating the circle *F* of diameter **2368**, the *gematria value* for 'Jesus Christ'.

The Hebrew word for 'Victory'*
(נצח[5]) has a *gematria value* of **148**.

Victory **148**

E

⟵ Square C **1,480** ⟶

⟵——— Circle *F* **2,368** ———⟶

Fig. 10.5
Victorious circles, Key E.

" *Nature is an infinite sphere whose center is everywhere and whose circumference is nowhere.* "
Blaise Pascal

* *See Gematria*   83

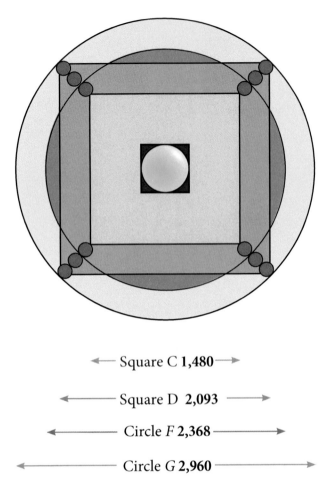

Square C **1,480**

Square D **2,093**

Circle F **2,368**

Circle G **2,960**

Fig. 10.6
Son of Man and victorious circles, Key F.

Two more circles of diameter **148** are placed on the corners of square C creating circle G of diameter **2,960**, surrounding square D. The *gematria value* for 'Son of Man'* (μιο στουανθρ ωπου⁶) is **2,960**.

The circles represent the spirit realm and the squares represent the physical realm, with measurements corresponding to significant *gematria values*. We have a square of edge length **1,480** equating to 'Christ'. We have a circle of diameter **2,368** equating to 'Jesus Christ', and a circle of edge length **2,960** equating to 'Son of Man'. The circle of diameter **888** represents 'Jesus'. This can be seen as different layers of the divine nature of a human being.

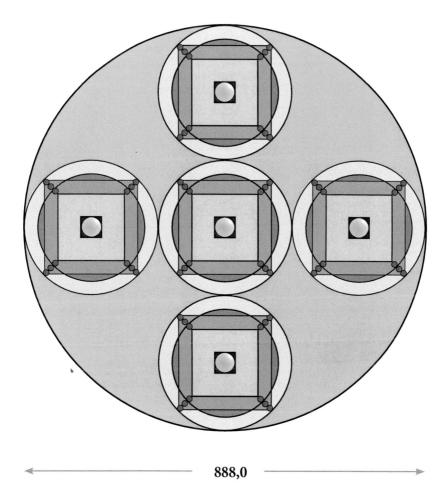

$888,0$

Fig. 10.7
*The circle of diameter **888,0**.*

The early Gnostic Christians made a mathematical metaphor out of the claim that Jesus 'rose' from the dead by 'raising' his living value **888** by a factor of **10**, making a circle with a circumference of **8,880** units depicting the 'raised' Jesus (**888 x 10** or **2,960** (Son of Man) x **3**).

The total sum of the *gematria values* of the **12** names of the tribes of Israel is **888,0**[*], Judah Ιουδα, Ruben Ρουβην, Gad Γαδ, Asher Ασηρ, Nepthalim Νεφθαλειμ, Manasses Μανασσης, Simeon Συμεων, Levi Λευι, Issachar Ισσαχαρ, Zebulon Ζαβουλων, Joseph Ιωσηφ, Benjamin Βενιαμιν[7].

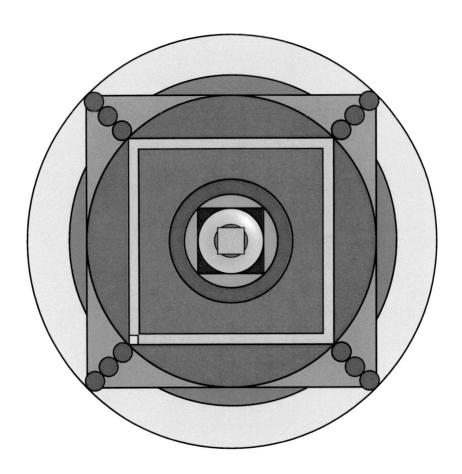

Fig. 10.8
Keys from A to F forming the universal architecture.

The Keys from *A* to *F* combine to form the universal architecture where the geometry of light is placed in the centre connecting with the *Etheric particle* and the geometric foundations from the harmonic numbers encoded in the Greek biblical scriptures.

The table in Figure 10.9 lists the extrapolated data from our planetary system on three different scales. The *Chi* (χ) scale is the distance in miles, the *Tau* (τ) scale is the distance in Egyptian digits (Fig 11.1) and the *Rho* (ρ) scale is expressed in reeds correlating with Ezekiel's description of the gifted land of edge length **25,000**.

Planets	Scale Chi (χ) miles	Scale Tau (τ) digits	Scale Rho (ρ)
Mercury	35,983,198	3.89	42.4
Venus	67,495,482	7.23	78.846
Sun	93,312,000	10	109.013
Mars	141,635,701	15.18	165.48
Planet X ?	201,553,920	21.6	235.45
Jupiter	483628133	51.829	565
Saturn	887076068	95	1035.616
Zodiacal sphere	895795200	96	1046.518

Fig. 10.9

The distance of planets from the Sun in a Geocentric Model.

On the *Tau* (τ) scale the distance of the Sun from Earth is **10**, in a Geocentric model with Earth being in the centre. The distance of the seventh planet Saturn from Earth is approximately **96**. Looking at Figure 10.4 in three dimensions, the large light blue square becomes a cube containing an orange sphere of radius **96**, representing the dome of the celestial or zodiacal sphere. The dimension of the zodiacal sphere is mirrored in Leonardo's *Vitruvian Man*. In Egyptian measurement his height of **6** feet can be broken down into "**96** digits" since a foot is equal to **16** digits or **24** palms.

On the *Rho* (ρ) scale the planetary system is expressed in reeds correlating to **2,093** being the diameter of the zodiacal sphere. The edge length of the outside wall of the *New Jerusalem* is **235.45** feet (Fig 8.5) which equates to **21.6** Egyptian digits on the *Tau* (τ) scale. Where the number **216 (6 x 6 x 6)** appears in the table above there is no known corresponding planet. This could possibly suggest the existence of a forgotten planet X between Mars and Jupiter exactly where we find the asteroid belt.

By doubling the last row we find the numbers **17,915,904,000** and **2,093**. The remarkable number **17,915,904,000** happens to be the diameter of the Sun **864,000** miles times **20,736**, two faces of *Hypercube 216*.

Fig. 10.10
*The Etheric Particle, Vitruvian Man, our planetary system
and the geometry of light embodied in the universal architecture.*

The outer circles of diameter **2,960** and **2,368** represent spheres beyond the
zodiacal sphere. The circumference of the orange circle in pale yellow represents
the orbit of Saturn and the edge of the zodiacal sphere. The circumference of the
light blue circle inscribed by *Vitruvian Man* has no corresponding planet. The
white circle just above the head of *Vitruvian Man* represents the orbit of Jupiter.
The next two black circles have no corresponding planets. The next circle in
gold tangent to the blue square represents the orbit of Planet X. The next four
circles represent the orbits of Mars (red circle), the Sun (yellow circle),Venus
(green circle) and Mercury (grey circle) with Earth at the center*.

Fig. 10.11

Rosslyn Chapel, Roslin, Midlothian: interior view,
showing ornate carvings and cusping.

"Architecture is the masterly, correct
and magnificent play of masses brought
together in light. Our eyes are made to see
forms in light; light and shade reveal these
forms; cubes, cones, spheres, cylinders or
pyramids are the great primary forms
which light reveals to advantage; the
image of these is distinct and tangible
within us without ambiguity. It is for this
reason that these are beautiful forms,
the most beautiful forms. Everybody is
agreed to that, the child, the savage and
the metaphysician."

Le Corbusier

Fig. 10.11
The Temple of man within the universal architecture.

When two Great Pyramids are superimposed on Figure 10.10, the sides of the pyramids touch the edge of the zodiacal sphere, creating a *Golden Diamond* representing the Temple of Man where *Christ Energy* emanates from the center.

11. Ancient Metrology

The units we find in ancient metrology contain many important numerical keys. The dimensions of the Temple of Solomon are based on ancient units coming originally from the dimensions of *Hypercube 216* (Fig 5.3). The Ancient Egyptians used a system of measurement based on **28** subdivisions called digits or a 'finger's breadth'. Our hands have **28** phalanges, a numerical key in the mathematical construct of the divine creation.

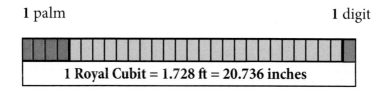

1 palm   1 digit

1 Royal Cubit = 1.728 ft = 20.736 inches

A finger's breadth

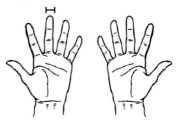

Fig. 11.1
The Ancient Egyptian Cubit.

The Sumerian cubit is **1.65888** ft which is ten thousandths of **165,888** (**82,944 x 2**). The Sumerian cubit is divided into **24** fingers with each finger equal to the Megalithic inch of **0.82944**.[1] The number **0.82944** is ten thousandths of **82,944** which is the volume of a single cube inside *Hypercube 216* in four dimensions (Fig 5.3).

In the Bible Ezekiel mentioned three units : the cubit, the cubit plus a hand's breadth (greater cubit) and the reed of six greater cubits (Ezekiel 40:13).

The Egyptian cubit, 1.728 ft = 0.526694 m.[2] This is exactly **20.736** inches. The harmonic number **20,736** represents two faces of *Hypercube 216*. The harmonic number **1,728** is a numerical key connecting the Earth's size in miles with the volume of the *Christ Sphere* in the *Etheric Particle* (Fig 9.6). The Egyptian cubit of **1.728** ft is equivalent to five hands of **0.3456** ft.

The Hebrew great cubit of six hands is one thousandth of **20,736** in feet. **2.0736 ft = 0.6320328 m.**

The reed of 6 great cubits is **12.4416 ft = 3.7921968 m** which is one ten thousandth of **124,416** in feet. The harmonic number **124,416** corresponds to twelve faces of *Hypercube 216* (surface area **10,368 x 12**) and can be expressed as **12 x 24 x 72**. Adding these numbers together results in the magical number **108**.

The digit or the finger's breadth is **0.740** inches which is **20.736** divided by **28**. Some ancient units of measurement are described below.

- **4** digits equals a palm.
- **12** digits or **3** palms equals a small span.
- **14** digits, one half a cubit, equals a large span.
- **16** digits or **4** palms equals one *t'ser.*
- **24** digits, or **6** palms equals a small cubit.

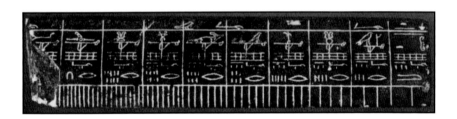

Fig. 11.2
Egyptian Cubit rod.

Figure 11.2 shows the end section of an Egyptian cubit rod. Starting from the right the 28th digit is divided into **2** parts, the 27th digit is divided into three parts, and so on until the 14th digit, divided into **16** parts. The smallest division being **1/16** of a digit, equal to **1/448** part of a Royal Cubit.[3]

$$1 \text{ digit} = 10,368 \div 14,000 \qquad (11)$$

The digit can also be calculated with the surface area of a face of *Hypercube 216*, **10,368** divided by **14,000**.

The Earth's mean radius of **14,000** multiplied by **864** cubits of **1.728** ft make **12,096,000** cubits or **20,901,888** ft.[4]

$$\textbf{1 digit} = 10,368 \div [20,901,888 \div (864 \times 1.728)]$$

$$\textbf{1 digit} = (186.624 \times 82,944) \div 20,901,888 \qquad (12)$$

In equation (12), **186,624** is the speed of light in miles per second in a vacuum and **82,944** is the volume of a single cube inside *Hypercube 216* in four dimensions (Fig 5.3).

$$\textbf{1 digit} = (186,624 \times 82,944) \div (1000 \times 20,901,888)$$

$$\textbf{1 digit} = (1,866,240 \times 107,495,424) \div (12,960,000 \times 20,901,888) \qquad (13)$$

In equation (13), **107,495,424** is the volume of *Hypercube 216* in four dimensions. In the Mayan calendar a time period of **12.96** baktuns (almost 13 as an integer number) is **1,866,240** days or **5,184** years. The number **12,960,000** appearing in equation (10) is a divisor of the distance traveled by light between the Sun and the galactic center in miles.

For some interpreters, **12,960,000** is considered to be Plato's number and was mentioned by Plato in his dialogue 'Republic' (8.546b–c). Below is a typical example of text from a recent translation.

> *"Now for divine begettings there is a period comprehended by a perfect number, and for mortal by the first in which augmentations dominating and dominated when they have attained to three distances and four limits of the assimilating and the dissimilating, the waxing and the waning, render all things conversable and commensurable [546c] with one another, whereof a basal four-thirds wedded to the pempad yields two harmonies at the third augmentation, the one the product of equal factors taken one hundred times, the other of equal length one way but oblong, one dimension of a hundred numbers determined by the rational diameters of the pempad lacking one in each case, or of the irrational lacking two; the other dimension of a hundred cubes of the triad. And this entire geometrical number is determinative of this thing, of better and inferior births."* [5]
>
> **Plato**

Other interpreters argued that Plato's number is **216**, being the cube of **6**, i.e. $6^3 = 216$ and also the sum of the cubes for the Pythagorean triple **(3, 4, 5)** :

$$3^3 + 4^3 + 5^3 = 6^3$$

The number **12,960,000** is also obtained through the Pythagorean triple **(3, 4, 5)** as the product of **3, 4** and **5**, power to four :

$$(3 \times 4 \times 5)^4 = 60^4$$

216 and **12,960,000** are two numerical keys of the mathematical construct of *Hypercube 216* and the *Etheric Particle*.

The transcendental number *Pi* (π) represents a key number bridging matter to spirit and approximately resolves the problem of squaring the circle. Metaphysically speaking, *Pi* (π) links the two different realms since the square represents energy on the physical level and the circle represents energy on the etheric level. Examining the value of *Pi* (π) from the perspective of *Hypercube 216*, a new value of *Pi* (π) can be calculated.

124,416 (12 faces of *Hypercube 216*) plus **2,808** (energy release of *Hypercube 216*) is equal to **127,224** which is a thousand times greater than *Xi* (ξ) **1.27224** equal to the ratio between the double height and base leg of the Great Pyramid (Fig 11.3). *Xi* (ξ) is also equal to the ratio between the diameter *D* of the circle circling a square of edge length *c* $72\sqrt{2}$, a face of *Hypercube 216* (Fig 11.4).

$$P(circle) = P(square) = \pi\, D(circle) = 288\sqrt{2} \text{ (squaring the circle)}$$

$$D(circle) \div c = 2H \div B = Xi\,(\xi) = 1.27224$$

$$Pi\,(\pi) = P(circle) \div D(circle) = P(circle) \div (\xi c) = 3.14406086 \qquad (14)$$

Gee Mister Spirit, there's a lot more to mathematics than two times two.
Donald Duck

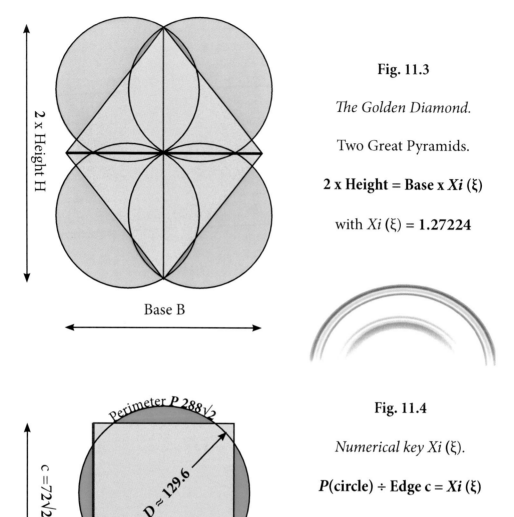

Fig. 11.3

The Golden Diamond.

Two Great Pyramids.

2 x Height = Base x *Xi* (ξ)

with *Xi* (ξ) = **1.27224**

Fig. 11.4

Numerical key Xi (ξ).

***P*(circle) ÷ Edge c = *Xi* (ξ)**

with *Xi* (ξ) = **1.27224**

A face of *Hypercube 216.*

The *Golden Diamond* is the energetic field surrounding everything in the universe. When a double rainbow appears, the human eye sees the first rainbow between **40** and **42** degrees and the second rainbow between **50** and **53** degrees. The Great Pyramid's slopes angles matches the angles necessary to perceive a rainbow (Fig 19.2). The double rainbow is an incredible example of divine manifestation in nature through the number **5,184** which is also half of the area of a face of *Hypercube 216,* and a key number in generating the seven colours of the rainbow.

The Megalithic Yard of **2.72** ft corresponds to the square root of **10** Egyptian digits shown in equation (15).

$$\sqrt{10} \textbf{ digits} = \sqrt{(10{,}368 \div 1{,}400)} = \textbf{2.721344 ft} \tag{15}$$

The value of **1** foot in meters is calculated with the numerical key **82,944** of *Hypercube 216* in equation (16).

$$\textbf{0.82944} \div \textbf{2.721344} = \textbf{0.30479 m} = \textbf{1 foot} \tag{16}$$

Ancient civilizations often laid out their stone circles in distances of Megalithic Yards suggesting that a high knowledge of mathematics and cosmology was available to them.

The following pendulum experiment shows further connections between *Hypercube 216* and the Megalithic Yard.

A pendulum swings a number of times **N** during a period of time **N** x **T** with **T** the period of time for a full swing back to the origin position. The period of time **T** and string length **L** is shown in equation (17).

$$T = 2\pi\sqrt{(L \div g)} \quad \text{with} \quad \pi = 4 \div \sqrt{\varphi} = \textbf{3.144605}^* \tag{17}$$

$$g = \textbf{9.81} \text{ m/s}^2 \text{ (gravity)}$$

Parameters	Experiment 1	Experiment 2	Experiment 3
Length **L** (m)	0.5	0.82944	1
Time **T** (sec)	1.419	1.82874	2.008

Fig. 11.5
Pendulum experiments with values L and T from equation (17).

A pendulum with a string length (**L**) of **1** meter takes just over **2** seconds to complete a swing. A pendulum with a string length equal to the Megalithic Yard or **0.82944** meters takes approximatively **1.83** seconds to complete a swing.

A pendulum with a string of length **L** swings from *B* to *C* and back again in a period of time T.

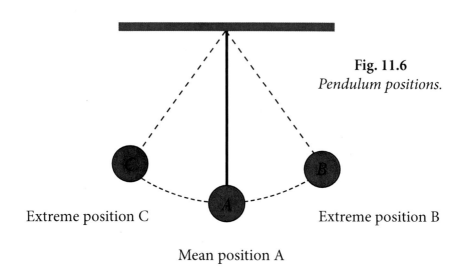

Fig. 11.6
Pendulum positions.

Extreme position C

Extreme position B

Mean position A

The period *T* can also be calculated with the harmonic number **666** and *Iota* (ι) the number of spins of *Hypercube 216* during a lunar day approximately equal to **7.714** (**216/28**) (Fig 5.6).

$$T = \sqrt{[(\sqrt{666}) \div (216/28)]} = \sqrt{[\sqrt{666} \div 7.714]} \approx 1.829 \text{ sec} \qquad (18)$$

The period *T* can be calculated approximately with **666** and the *Golden Ratio Phi* (φ) **1.618**.

$$T = \sqrt{(666 \div \varphi^{11})} \approx 1.829 \text{ sec} \qquad (19)$$

The pendulum takes approximately **364** seconds to swing **199** times. The total period of **364** seconds (*N* x *T*) can be calculated with the period *T* of **1.82874** seconds and **666** shown in equation (20).

$$666 \div T \approx 364.2 \text{ sec} \qquad (20)$$
$$365.24 \div T \approx 199.8 = 66.6 \text{ x } 3 \qquad (21)$$

The pendulum takes approximately **365** seconds to swing **200** times. The total period of **365** seconds (*N* x *T*) can be calculated with the period *T* of **1.82874** sec and **66.6** shown in equation (21).

The mean time value between **364.2** and **365.24** seconds is approximately **364.8** seconds which is **6.08** minutes. This period of **6** minutes is the time frame for the Sun and Moon to move **1.5** degrees across the sky on spring equinox, when both have the same apparent angular diameter of **0.5** degrees* (equivalent to one lunar or solar diameter).

Six minutes is the time for the shadow of a standing stone to pass through **1.5** degrees on a circular template.

Fig. 11.7
Gnomon on a sundial.
St. Michael's Mount,
Cornwall, England.

Fig. 11.8
Three stones in Stanton Drew.

A group of three stones, known as 'The Cove', in the garden of the Druids Arms pub.

On equinoxes and solstices, there is an accumulation of etheric energy at specific energy points on the Earth.

Ancient civilizations built megalithic standing stones at these locations in order to manipulate energy coming through the *ether*.

The number of spins of *Hypercube 216* is *Iota* (ι) **7.714** (Fig 5.6) in **24** hours or **1,440** minutes. The number of spins is approximately **0.03257** in a period of **6** minutes. This calculation is shown in equation (22).

$$(6.08 \times 7.714) \div 1,440 \approx 1 \div 30.7 \approx 0.03257 \qquad (22)$$

The number of spins of **0.03257** in **6** minutes multiplied by *Phi* (φ) **1.618** power to **23** results in the edge length of a single cube inside *Hypercube 216* equal to **12√2** shown in equation (23).

$$0.03257 \times \varphi^{23} \approx 12\sqrt{2} \text{ at } 0.018\,\% \qquad (23)$$

Hypercube 216 spins **17** times in approximately **521** minutes. It would spin **72√2** times in approximately **3,168** minutes, **72√2** being the edge length of *Hypercube 216* and **3,168** being the *gematria value* for 'Lord Jesus Christ'*.

One spin of *Hypercube 216* lasts a time period of **186.666** minutes which is approximately one thousandth of **186,624** the speed of light in miles per second or **187**, the edge length of the inside court of the first Temple of Solomon in cubits.

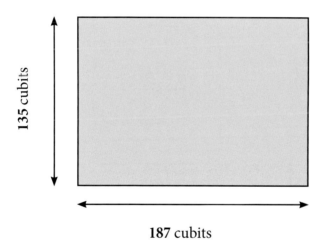

187 cubits

Fig. 11.9
The dimensions of the inside court of the first Temple of Solomon.

The area of the inside court is **135** multiplied by **186.666** resulting in **25,200** squared cubits. The harmonic number **252** is the *gematria value* for 'Light'* (המאור[6]). **25,200** is also **5,040** multiplied by **5**. The Earth's radius **3960** miles added to the moon's radius **1,080** miles is **5040** miles.

"Only the existence of a field of force can account for the motions of the bodies as observed, and its assumption dispenses with space curvature. All literature on this subject is futile and destined to oblivion. So are all attempts to explain the workings of the universe without recognizing the existence of the ether and the indispensable function it plays in the phenomena. (...) There is no energy in matter other than that received from the environment."

Nicolas Tesla

The *ether* has been discussed by meta-physicians, alchemists and magicians for a very long time. Plato spoke about this element. In his reasoning he discerned three kinds of air; higher air, atmospheric air and air mist. He specified with Aristotle and others that the *ether* is a fifth element wherein the celestial bodies move in a variety of spiraling air. Aristotle affirmed that the soul has its origin in the fifth element. The Ancient Greek etymology for *ether* is 'burn'. Philip of Opus described the *ether* as a form of fire.

There are different stages of embryonic cell division corresponding to the growing divisions of a circle beginning with the *Vesica Piscis* and forming the *Seed of Life* pattern.

There is a fundamental and important relationship between frequency and geometry.

Each stage of embryonic cell division vibrates at a different frequency showing a different geometric form.

Fig. 12.1
The different stages of embryonic cell division.

Form is a direct result of vibration and vibration is a direct function of form. Each form has its own frequency, a certain vibration supposedly emitted from the center of its body. Plato made a correspondence between geometry and the elements based on the knowledge of Alchemy.

In Alchemy there are seven major metals, each one of them related to its own state of matter, color and chakra. There are seven major chakras, organs in the body and celestial bodies in Astronomy.

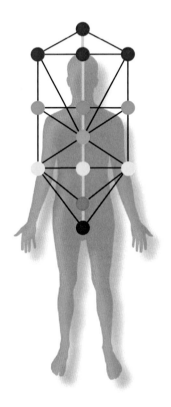

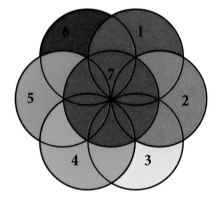

Fig. 12.2
The seven colors.

In the human body there are seven *chakra wheels* vibrating at different frequencies positioned on the central axis of the tree of life shown in the geometric pattern of the *Kabbalah*.

Each color of the *Seed of Life* pattern is related to one of the seven planets, chakras and metals listed in Figure 9.5.

Fig. 12.3
The seven chakra wheels and the Kabbalah in the human body.

"Numbers constitute the only universal language."

Nathanael West

> "*The alchemical operation consisted essentially in separating the prima materia, the so-called chaos, into the active principle, the soul, and the passive principle, the body, which were then reunited in personified form in the coniunctio or 'chymical marriage'... the ritual cohabitation of Sol and Luna.*"[1]
>
> **Carl Jung**

The fifth element is the medium through which everything exists and comes forth. It is also seen as the primeval waters representing the mysteries of the cosmos and chaos. Ancient Egyptian cosmogony was based on knowledge of the cosmos. It stated that first there was darkness and a primeval ocean known as 'Nun' and related to the forces of chaos. This primeval waters could be considered as the female fluid from which things are born. From the primeval water emerged the Lotus, an important symbol representing the Sun, rebirth, regeneration and reincarnation. The water lily is also used to represent this emergence. The Lotus is therefore a symbol from which the life force emanates and can be seen as the *Etheric Particle*.

The *Etheric Particle* encodes the number seven. Planets, chakras, colors of the rainbow, days of the week and metals are usually found in groups of seven.

	Planets	Chakras	Colors	Metals
1.	Mars	Mooladhara	Red	Iron
2.	Moon	Swadhishthan	Orange	Silver
3.	Sun	Nabhi	Yellow	Gold
4.	Venus	Anahat	Green	Copper
5.	Jupiter	Vishuddhi	Blue	Tin
6.	Saturn	Agnya	Indigo	Lead
7.	Mercury	Sahasrara	Purple	Mercury

Fig. 12.4
The number seven.

Seven shades of color appear in a specific order during the alchemical process.

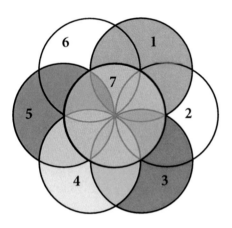

1. Earth is light red.
2. Water is white.
3. Fire is red.
4. Air is citrine.
5. Dark water is black.
6. White water is a perfect white.
7. Universal consciousness is quicksilver.

Fig. 12.5
Alchemy of Consciousness.

In the seventh circle where there is an overlapping of three or four colors, the resulting color is quicksilver, a color between black and white. Quicksilver is the old name for the metal mercury.

1. The physical realm : earth, air, fire and water.
2. The etheric realm beyond the four elements : dark water (primeval ocean), evolved water and universal consciousness.

	Colors	Elements	Gender	Character
1.	Slightly red	Earth	Feminine	Cold and Dry
2.	White	Water	Feminine	Cold and Wet
3.	Red	Fire	Masculine	Hot and Dry
4.	Citrine	Air	Masculine	Hot and Wet
5.	Blackness	Primeval Ocean	Feminine	Chaos
6.	Nearly white	Evolved Water	Masculine	Order
7.	Quicksilver	Universal Consciousness	Merging	The All

Fig. 12.6
The alchemical process of the elements.

Mathematics and geometry show an existence of higher planes or dimensions connected to the physical world. Leonardo's *Vitruvian Man* has two bodies represented by the square and the circle or the cube and the sphere in three dimensions. The cube represents the physical body (tangible matter) and the sphere represents the etheric body (light body or intangible matter).

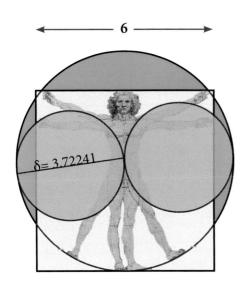

Two *Great Lights* in green
of diameter *Delta* δ.

Fig. 12.7
*The physical and light body of
the Vitruvian Man.*

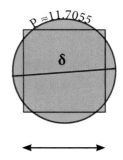

Edge length E of the square.
$E ≈ 784/268$

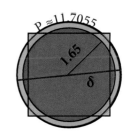

A *Great Light*
Squaring the circle

The *Great Light* is the circle of diameter *Delta* (δ) equal to **3.72241** (shown in green). The diameter of the turquoise sphere inscribed by the *Vitruvian Man* is approximately **7.4422**. The *gematria value* for 'Two Great Lights'* (הגדלים המאורות²) is **744**.

The orange square of edge length E has the same area as the blue circle of radius of **1.65**.

$$E^2 = \pi \, m^2 \quad \text{with} \quad m^2 ≈ 2.72 \quad \text{and} \quad m ≈ 1.65 \qquad (23)$$

Since we know the volume of the sphere inscribed by *Vitruvian Man* to be **216** cubic feet, the radius of the sphere *Delta* (δ) can be calculated through the following equation.

$$V = (4 \div 3) \, \pi \, \delta^3 \quad \Rightarrow \quad \delta = [3 \div (4\pi V)]^{1/3} \approx 3.72241 \qquad (24)$$

$$\delta^4 = 192$$

Equation (24) uses *Pi* (π) with a value of **3.1446055***.

Some interesting correlations appear between the four following mathematical constants in equations (25) and (26); the *Golden Ratio Phi* (φ), *Euler's* constant *e*, *Pi* (π) and the diameter of *the Great Light Delta* (δ).

$$\delta \, e \, \pi^2 \approx 100 \quad \text{with} \quad e = 2.71828 \quad \text{and} \quad \pi = 3.1446055 \qquad (25)$$

The interior angle of a seven pointed star **51.48°** is very close to the slope angle of the Great Pyramid **51.84°** and can be calculated in the following equation.

$$\varphi \, e \, \pi \, \delta = 51.48° \approx 360 \div 7 \approx 51.43 \qquad (26)$$

The first verse of the Bible reads "In the beginning God created the heavens and the earth" (את השמים ואת הארץ בראשית ברא אלהים³) and has a total *gematria value* of **2,701**. There are twenty eight letters and seven Hebrew words, both important numbers seen in the *Etheric Particle*.

2,701 is **37** multiplied by **73**. The mirror numbers **37** and **73** are the **12**th and **21**st prime numbers, again mirrors. This mirroring continues with **144** (**12** squared) and **441** (**21** squared).

From the One come the three primary colours which then form the seven colours of the rainbow. The numbers **37** and **73** can be calculated with the constants *Phi* (φ), *e*, *Pi* (π), *Delta* (δ) and *m*.

$$\delta^2 \, \varphi \, m \approx 37 \qquad \pi^2 \, e^2 \approx 73 \qquad \delta^2 \, \varphi \, m \, \pi^2 \, e^2 \approx 2,701 \qquad (27)$$

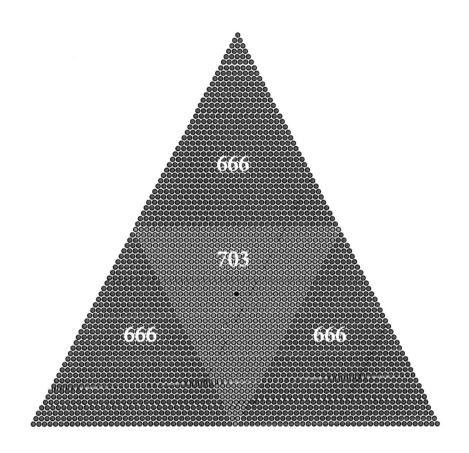

Fig. 12.8
The triangular number 73 (73 lines in total).

Geometrically, the triangular number **73** has **2,701** energy points (dots) making three orange triangles of **666** (triangular number **36**) and a central green triangle of **703** (triangular number **37**).

The harmonic numbers **666** and **703** are fundamental blocs of the mathematical construct of creation characterising solar or pyramid energy. **666** is a fundamental number in the *Etheric Particle* (Fig 8.1) and the *universal architecture* (Fig 10.10).

In the green triangle there is one central red point, a gravity centre, surrounded by **702** points. The voltage energy frequency of **2,808** (**702** times **4**) from *Hypercube 216* has an equivalent mass of **82,944** (equation 3).

The triangular number **73** forms a pyramid of **2,701** spheres, each with a volume of **216**. The total volume of these spheres make a larger sphere representing the heavens and earth. The radius is calculated in the following equation.

$$V = 2{,}701 \times 216 = 583{,}416$$

$$V = (4/3)\,\pi\,r^3 = 583{,}416 \qquad \Rightarrow \qquad r \approx 51.84 \qquad (28)$$

The radius of the sphere is approximately **51.84**, the slope angle of the Great Pyramid or one hundredth of **5,184** half the area of a face of *Hypercube 216*.

In Ancient Egypt the numbers **23** and **28** were very important. **28** is the total number of digits in the ancient system of measurement defining the sacred Royal Cubit (Fig 11.1). **28** multiplied by the *Light Body Constant Delta* (δ) squared approximates to **388**, the *gematria value* for 'Scarlet Thread'* (חוט השני⁴).

$$28\,\delta^2 \approx 388 \qquad (29)$$

388 is **365** added to **23** and the number of solar days in a year. The tilt axis of Earth is an angle of approximately **23** degrees**.

$$388 = 365 + 23 \qquad (30)$$

388 divided by *Pi* (π) reveals the harmonic number read from the top to the base of the *Tetractys* **1,234** (Fig 1.1).

$$388 \div \pi \approx 123.4 \qquad (31)$$

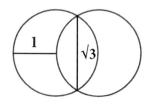

Delta (δ) in Sacred Geometry

$$\delta^2 = 8\sqrt{3} \qquad (32)$$

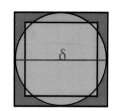

Fig. 12.9
Sacred Geometry and the Great Light.

The harmonic number **1,234** is a numerical key of the *Etheric Particle* and the *Sacred Angle* from the seven pointed star **308.571** multiplied by 4 and **1,234** can be calculated with the perimeter *P* of the *Great Light*.

$$9\,P = 9\,(\delta\,\pi)^2 \approx 1{,}234.2857 \tag{32}$$

The number **23** is calculated with the *Light Body constant Delta* (δ) **3.72241** and the *Golden Ratio Phi* (φ) **1.618**.

$$10\,\delta \div \varphi = 10\,\delta\,\phi \approx 23 \quad \text{with} \quad \phi = 1 \div \varphi = 0.618 \tag{33}$$

Fig. 12.10
23 degrees in Ancient Egypt.

The angle of inclination between Osiris' hat and the vertical axis is **23**. His arms also make this angle.

Osiris was the initiator of numbers based on **9** and the fractal of numbers coming from *Hypercube 216*. This ancient knowledge comes through Egypt from the continent of Atlantis.

Number fractals allow us to define the measurement of units used by the Ancients in their temples and calendars.

Awareness of this ancient knowledge allows us to contemplate deeper into the unification of matter and spirit, reminding us of our divine natural ability to connect with all things in the universe.

> *"The harmony of the world is made manifest in form and number, and the heart and soul and all the poetry of natural philosophy are embodied in the concept of mathematical beauty."*
>
> **Sir D'Arcy Wentworth Thompson**

> *".... 192 = MAPIAM, the name of Mary, the Mother of Jesus, here symbolic of His Church"* [5]
>
> **Bligh Bond & Lea**

13. Light Codes of the Ether

The light codes of the capstone of the Great Pyramid are mathematically encoded in the number of spiral arcs forming a seven-pointed star as an expression of the divine blueprint. A spiral arc is defined as the pathway for the ether to flow from one *Zero Energy Point* to a seventh point.

The number seven has some interesting mathematical properties. Any number non divisible by **7** gives the sequence **142,857** repeated infinitely. An example is shown in equation (33).

$$153 \div 7 = 21.857142857142857 \ldots \tag{33}$$

The number **142,857** is related to the *Light Body Constant Delta* (δ) (Fig 12.7) and **744** shown in equation (34).

$$744\, \delta^4 + 9 = 142{,}857 \ \text{ with } \ \delta^4 = 192 \tag{34}$$

The spiralling *ether* can be quantified as **14** spiral arcs with a total of **98** energy points (**7 x 14**) (Fig. 13.2). There is one more energy point needed to reach **99** to close the first level. The second level is another run of **14** spiral arcs with **196** energy points (**7 x 28**). There are two extra energy points needed to close the second level **198** (**2 x 99**). The third level reaches the **294**[th] energy point (**7 x 42**) with three extra energy points needed to close the third level **297** (**3 x 99**).

Finally the *n*-level has *n* multiplied by **98** energy points with *n* energy points needed to close the *n*-level.

Figure 13.1 lists the light codes up to the **14**[th] level. The **14**[th] level is the closure of the **13** levels of **99** energy points.

The last column lists the values of the remainder after the number of energy points has been divided by **7** (modulo 7). For example **495** is equal to **70** multiplied by **7** with remainder **5** (**495 [7] = 5**).

Levels	Energy Points	Spiral arcs	Closure	Closure minus Energy Points	Remainder modulo 7
1st	98	14	99	1	1
2nd	196	28	198	2	2
3rd	294	42	297	3	3
4th	392	56	396	4	4
5th	490	70	495	5	5
6th	588	84	594	6	6
7th	686	98	693	7	0
8th	784	112	792	8	1
9th	882	126	891	9	2
10th	980	140	990	10	3
11th	1,078	154	1,089	11	4
12th	1,176	168	1,188	12	5
13th	1,274	182	1,287	13	6
Total				91	42
14th			1,296		

Fig. 13.1

The light codes of the ether with seven energy points.

The closure of the **13** levels requires **9** further energy points to reach **1,296 (6 x 6 x 6 x 6)** which is one fourth of **5,184.**

The light code **142,857** contains the sequence **1 42 85 7.**

The harmonic numbers **42** and **85** are positioned between the numbers **1** and **7.** There are **42** energy points to reach the **6**th sub level (Fig. 13.2) and **85** to begin the **12**th.

According to the *Hitchhiker's Guide to the Galaxy* the answer to the ultimate question of life, the universe and everything is **42**. The total in the last column in Figure 13.1 is **42**.

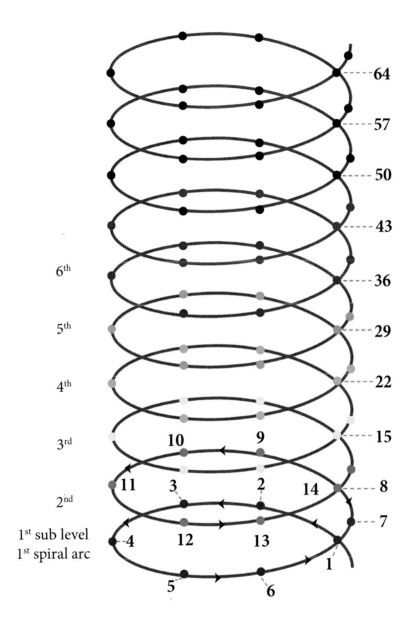

Fig. 13.2
The spiralling ether from a three dimensional view.

Figure 13.2 shows the number of energy points of a spiral. Beginning on the first sub-level, the *ether* spirals through seven energy points continuing up through a total of **70** energy points (**10** sub-levels).

Levels	Energy Points	Spiral arcs	Closure	Fractal Closure x 111 (37 x 3)
1st	98	14	99	10,989
2nd	196	28	198	21,978
3rd	294	42	297	32,967
4th	392	56	396	43,956
5th	490	70	495	54,945
6th	588	84	594	65,934
7th	686	98	693	76,923
8th	784	112	792	87,912
9th	882	126	891	98,901
10th	980	140	990	109,890
11th	1,078	154	1,089	120,879
12th	1,176	168	1,188	131,868
13th	1,274	182	1,287	**142,857**
14th			1,296	143,856
Total				

Fig. 13.3
*The light codes of the ether ending in **142,857** and **143,856** from multiplying the Closure column by **111**.*

The cosmic code **142,857** is **1,287** multiplied by **111**. The physical body of *Vitruvian Man* inside a cube of edge length **6** feet has a volume of **1,296** in four dimensions (Fig 5.3).

The key to the fourth dimension is **1,296**.

114

The light code **143,856** contains the sequence **1 43 85 6**. The harmonic numbers **43** and **85** are positioned between the numbers **1** and **6**. A spiral arc is completed by six energy points. There are **43** energy points to reach the 7th sub level and **85** to begin the **14th**.

Levels	Energy Points	Spiral arcs	Closure	Closure minus Energy Points	Remainder modulo 7
1st	96	16	99	3	3
2nd	192	32	198	6	6
3rd	288	48	297	9	9
4th	384	64	396	12	3
5th	480	80	495	15	6
6th	576	96	594	18	9
7th	672	112	693	21	3
8th	768	128	792	24	6
9th	864	144	891	27	9
10th	960	160	990	30	3
11th	1,056	176	1,089	33	6
12th	1,152	192	1,188	36	9
13th	1,248	208	1,287	39	3
14th			1,296		9
Total				273	84

Fig. 13.4
The light codes for spiral arcs with six energy points.

The total of the remainder modulo 7 is **84** and the total of the Closure column is **273**.

The harmonic number **143,856** is an important light code connected with the numbers **666** and **216** shown in the following equation.

$$143,856 = 216 \times 666 = 6^3 \times 666 \qquad (35)$$

The harmonic number **273** is key in the process of manifestation :

- The sunspot rotational period is **27.3** days.
- The orbital period of the moon is **27.3** days.
- The moon and Earth's diameter ratio is **0.273** (Fig 1.8).
- Water liquefies **273°** above Absolute Zero.
- The human menstrual cycle is **27.3** days.
- The human gestation period is **273** days.

Fig. 13.5
Leonardo da Vinci's painting of the Last Supper.

Much has been written about this famous painting but what has been ignored is the large **10,101** structure behind the feast. There are three huge doorways behind Jesus and his disciples. These doorways can be interpreted as etheric gates or portals connecting to higher dimensions.

The painting is **880** cm wide and **460** cm high. These two numbers are encoded in the Great Pyramid. Half the circumference of the base of the Great Pyramid is **880** cubits or **460** meters (**880 x 1.715 x 0.3048**). The cubit is equal to **1.715** ft which is close to the Egyptian cubit of **1.728** ft defined in Figure 11.1. **460** and **880** express the same length in different units.

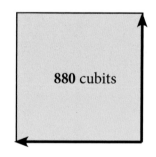

Fig. 13.6
*Base of
the Great Pyramid.*

The number **10,101** represents the number **21** in binary as shown in equation (36). The harmonic number **21** is a numerical key for the entrance points of energy on Earth through the three cosmic gates found in a variety of ancient sacred sites.

$$2^4 \times 1 + 2^3 \times 0 + 2^2 \times 1 + 2^1 \times 0 + 2^0 \times 1 = 21 \qquad (36)$$

Step Pyramid of Djoser
in Saqqara, Egypt.

Temple of Kukulkan
in Mexico.

Prasat Thom Koh Ker
in Cambodia

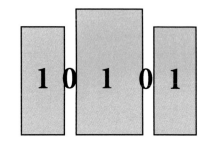

Three gates in South
America, Pre-inca

Three gates in Saqqara

Fig. 13.7
The three cosmic gates in sacred sites.

The most important divisors in the number **10,101** are **273** and **37**, the numerical foundation of light (equation 27).

$$10,101 = 111 \times 91 = 777 \times 13 = 273 \times 37 = 21 \times 13 \times 37 \qquad (37)$$

The *first star number* is **1** energy point.

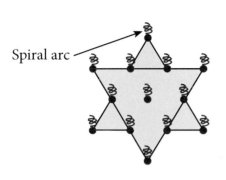

Spiral arc

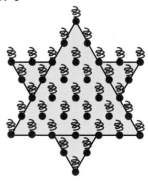

The *second star number*
has **13** energy points.

The *third star number*
has **37** energy points.

Fig. 13.8
Energy emanation points on the six pointed star.

Spiral arcs emanate from each energy point on the star. The *second star* has **13** energy points each with a blue spiral. The *third star* has **37** energy points. For three sub levels each blue spiral passes through **21** energy points resulting in a total of **273 (21 x 13)** energy points.

On the right hand star fractalling out are **273** energy points for each energy point resulting in **10,101 (273 x 37)**.

The total number of spiral arcs to reach the **99**th energy point is *Beta* (β) shown in equation (38).

$$99 = 14 \times 7 + 1 = 7\beta \quad \text{with} \quad \beta = 14 + 1 \div 7 = 14.142857... \quad (38)$$

Equation (39) shows the relationship between the light codes **10,101** and **142,857** with *Beta* (β).

$$10,101\,\beta = 142,857 \quad (39)$$

The number **273** can be calculated with the *Light Body Constant Delta* (δ) **3.72241**, the *Golden Ratio Phi* (φ) (**1.618**) and the number **28**.

$$28\,\delta\,\varphi^2 \approx 273 \quad (40)$$

118

The light code **143,856** (or **1,296 x 111**) represents the missing capstone of the Great Pyramid and *the Missing Cube.*

The capstone of the Great Pyramid amplified the capacity for the geometry to harness earth (Yin) and cosmic (Yang) energies, allowing access to the higher dimensions through our physical and light bodies, commencing with the fourth dimension.

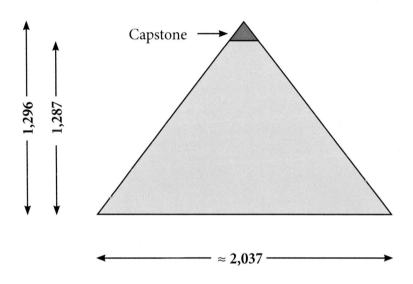

Fig. 13.9
The capstone of the Great Pyramid.

The golden age of Aquarius heralds a time when the capstone will return to its original place on the top of the Great Pyramid. Light codes operating in the planetary grid will bridge the third dimension to higher dimensions leading to a whole new experience for humanity.

> *"Everything in the Universe, throughout all its kingdoms, is conscious: i.e., endowed with a consciousness of its own kind and on its own plane of perception."* **H.P. Blavatsky**

The number **9** is a powerful number operating in the Divine creation through which the numeric blueprint **142,857** represents the infinite energy flow coming from the primordial ocean. A geometric pattern of this flow can be seen through the nonagon (**9** sided-gon) and is called the Enneagram. It begins with **1** and follows the numerical sequence **142,857**.

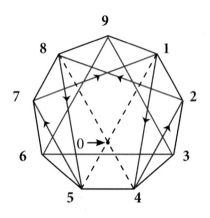

Fig 13.10

The Enneagram

The numbers **3**, **6** and **9** operate in the unmanifested world whereas the numbers **1**, **4**, **2**, **8**, **5** and **7** operate in the manifested world. The energetic flow traces the gateway from where the *Zero Energy Point* can be located above the base of the triangle **3-6-9**.

The cosmic code **142,857** is the blueprint of the *ether* related to the number **7** operating in the divine system based on the number **9**.

The numbers **3**, **6** and **9** work together to conduct the energetic flow from the *Zero Energy Point* within the toroidal energetic field surrounding every conscious cell in the universe. There is an infinite cycle of energy flow happening simultaneously, energy in and out, self sustaining to allow a perfect equilibrium between Yin and Yang.

The balance of Yin and Yang energy creates a third field representing the quality and union of these two.

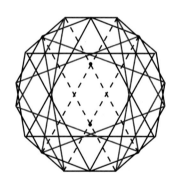

Fig 13.11

The third field created in the divine blueprint of 9.

" *If you only knew the magnificence of the 3, 6 and 9, then you would have a key to the universe.*"

Nikola Tesla

14. Ancient Calendars

The Mayan calendar is based on harmonic numbers from *Hypercube 216* (Fig 5.3). An era of **12.96** (almost 13) Baktuns is **5,184** years, a number representing half the surface area of a face of *Hypercube 216*.

The number **5,184** is found in the slope angle of the Great Pyramid (**51.84°**) suggesting that the Egyptians and the Mayans shared a mutual knowledge of the divine source.

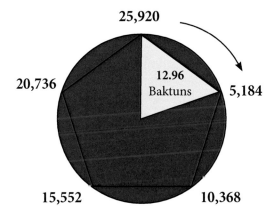

One Baktun = **400** years
400 x **12.96** = **5,184**
144,000 Mayan days

A Mayan year
20 x 12.96 = 259.2 days

Fig. 14.1
The Great Year of 25,920 years.

With a lunar year of **360** days, **12.96** Baktuns is **1,866,240** days. Remarkably **1,866,240** is **10** times the speed of light in miles per second. The Earth's axis rotates (precesses) like a spinning top*. The period of precession of the equinoxes or the Great Year is **25,920** years, a cycle of five periods of **5,184** years or five periods of **12.96** Baktuns. One twelfth of **25,920** is **2160** years or **30°** of a circle. **2,160** is the diameter of the Moon in miles.

The *Etheric Particle* has **12** moons around Earth encoding the Great Year of **25,920** years since **12** multiplied by **2,160** is **25,920** (Fig 8.1). The Mayan year of **259.2** days and the Great Year of **25,920** years are clearly fractals of the number **2,592**.

400 is **20** squared, a number reflected in the **20** cubit edge length of the sanctuary of the Holy Temple of Solomon**.

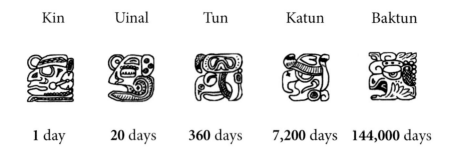

Kin	Uinal	Tun	Katun	Baktun
1 day	20 days	360 days	7,200 days	144,000 days

Fig. 14.2
Long Count Glyphs and values in days.

Above are five components of the Mayan Calendar. The last two can be found from Tun by multiplying by **20**.
360 x 20 = 7,200 days defined as **1** Katun, etc. The Mayans used a calendar in base **5** within a base **20**. Each unit has a time period based upon the number **9** except for the two first units Uinal and Kin.

144,000 (1+4+4 = 9)   **7,200** (7 + 2 = 9)   **360** (3 + 6 = 9)

In the Mayan Calendar, there are nine stages of consciousness from the beginning of the creation of the universe. The time period of these stages in lunar days encodes the great harmonic numbers connected with the dimensions of *Hypercube 216*, the precession of the equinoxes and the distances in miles between the Earth, Sun and Moon.

The numbers defining the time period of the nine cycles of consciousness are **12.96** and **20**. The time period for the last stage of consciousness is **233.28** days (**12.96 x 18** kin) represented by the top step of a pyramid (Fig 13.3). The distance between Earth and Moon is exactly **233,280** miles (Fig 9.3), a thousand times greater than **233.28**. The second from highest step represents a time period of **4665.6** days (**12.96 x 360**) or **12.96** Mayan years. The third step from the top lasts **93,312** days (**12.96 x 7,200**) or **259.2** Mayan years. The distance between the Earth and Sun is exactly **93,312,000** miles (Fig 9.4), a thousand times greater than **93,312** and one hundredth of the **9,331,200** days in the Great Year (**25,920 x 360**).

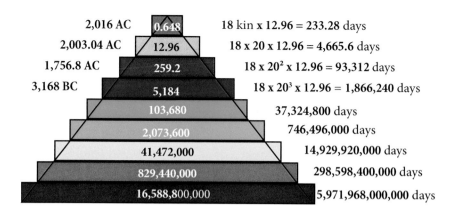

			2,016 AC	0.648		18 kin x 12.96 = 233.28 days
		2,003.04 AC		12.96		18 x 20 x 12.96 = 4,665.6 days
	1,756.8 AC			259.2		18 x 20² x 12.96 = 93,312 days
3,168 BC				5,184		18 x 20³ x 12.96 = 1,866,240 days
				103,680		37,324,800 days
				2,073,600		746,496,000 days
				41,472,000		14,929,920,000 days
				829,440,000		298,598,400,000 days
				16,588,800,000		5,971,968,000,000 days

Fig. 14.3
*Nine stepped Temple of Kukulkan
encoding the nine cycles of consciousness.*

	Colour	Baktuns	Years	Great Years	Equivalence
1	Red	41,472,000	16,588,800,000	640,000	1.65888 ft
2	Orange	2,073,600	829,440,000	32,000	82,944 units
3	Yellow	103,680	41,472,000	1,600	10,368 units
4	Green	5,184	2,073,600	80	51.84°
5	Turquoise	259.2	103,680	4	25,920 years
6	Blue	12.96	5,184	0.2	51.84°
7	Purple	0.648	259.2	0.01	25,920 years
8	Golden	0.0324	12.96	0.0005	129.6 units
9	Grey	0.0162	0.648	0.000025	Phi ≈ 1.62

Fig. 14.4 *The Mayan Long Count Calendar.*

1.65888 ft - Sumerian Cubit (Chapter 12)

82,944 - Volume of a single cube inside *Hypercube 216* in 4D

10,368 - Surface area of a face of *Hypercube 216*

51.84 - Slope angle the Great Pyramid in degrees

25,920 - The Great Year

1,296 - Light code of the *ether* and key to the 4th dimension

162 - Equation (2)

The nine steps of consciousness are happening simultaneously. Each step has a different length to mark the speed and time period of conscious evolution throughout the ages.

The pyramid is the representation of a cosmic clock related to the three dimensional experience. On a cosmic scale the number **9** symbolizes the completion of a great era of billions of years and the beginning of a higher dimensional experience. The construction of the Great Pyramid clearly shows that humanity did not evolve in a linear fashion.

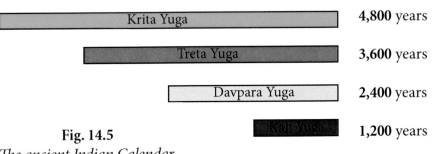

Krita Yuga	**4,800** years
Treta Yuga	**3,600** years
Davpara Yuga	**2,400** years
Kali Yuga	**1,200** years

Fig. 14.5
The ancient Indian Calendar.

The sacred scriptures of India known as the *Puranas* speak of the four 'ages of the earth' called Yugas. The sum of these four ages makes **12,000** 'divine years'. This is clearly another ancient calendar system based on the dimensions of *Hypercube 216*.

The *Puranas* tell us that 'One year of the mortals is equal to one day of the gods'.[1] One day of the gods equates to **360** mortal days. A year of the gods equates to **129,600** mortal days (**360 x 360**), a fractal of **12.96** Mayan Baktuns.

The *Krita Yuga* is a time period of **1,728,000** mortal years (**4,800 x 360**). **1,728,000** is a fractal of the Royal Egyptian Cubit of **1.728** feet.
The *Treta Yuga* is a time period of **12,960,000** mortal years. This is Plato's famous number from his text *Republic 546b–c* according to some interpreters (Chapter 11).

The *Davpara Yuga* is a time period of **864,000** mortal years which is also the Sun's diameter in miles (Figs 9.4 and 9.5).
Finally the *Kali Yuga* is a time period of **432,000** mortal years, **432** being half of **864**, both musical notes of A in Hertz.

124

One Mahayuga is equivalent to **12,000** divine years or **4,320,000** mortal years. A day of *Brahma* is equivalent to **1,000** *Mahayugas* or **4,320,000,000** mortal years. The completion of the Mayan Calendar is **3.84** days of *Brahma* resulting in **16,588,800,000** mortal years.

$$4{,}320{,}000{,}000 \times 3.84 = 16{,}588{,}800{,}000 \qquad (41)$$

82,944, the volume of a single cube in four dimensions inside *Hypercube 216*, divided by **216** is **384** (Fig 5.3). The famous Pythagorean G is **384** Hz on a C scale from **64** Hz.

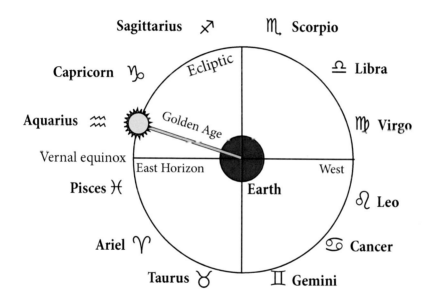

Fig. 14.6
The Wheel of time.

In my opinion the solar system enters a photon band at the beginning of the age of Aquarius. The Egyptians and Mayans used harmonic numbers encoded in the cycles of the cosmos. The Egyptians built the Great Sphinx facing directly East which may have represented a Lion further back in time. The Lion refers to the Great Transitions during a Great Year of **25,920** years. The Sphinx faces East waiting for the great return of the Golden Age and the completion of the Mayan Calendar, **3.84** Days of Brahma.

Fig. 14.7
The Great Sphinx.

There were twelve disciples of Jesus making a circle of **12** around the **13th** person. Similarly the *Etheric Particle* has **12** moons around Earth. There are said to be **13** crystal skulls that will be gathered together again in order to release the ancient knowledge for the Golden Age. This knowledge comes from the ancient civilizations of Atlantis, Lemuria, Mu and possibly others further back in time.

Fig. 14.8
Tibetan Crystal Skull Amar.

"The cross is the symbol of the Christian faith in immortal life, just as the crystal skulls are the same symbol of the immortality of the human spirit. The skulls represent the Native American faith in the intangible force that all religions call God, the Creator, the Maker, and we call the Great Mystery or Great Spirit. (...) Like the cross, the crystal skull is a symbol of transformation. It is an image of death that is transparent. It shows us that death is not a place of darkness and gloom but a place of crystal clarity and illumination."[5]
Jamie Sams

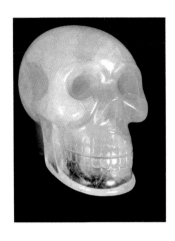

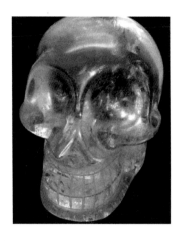

Fig. 14.9
Einstein the crystal skull.

Fig. 14.10
Bob the crystal skull.

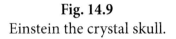

"The Mayan Calendar is above all else a prophetic calendar that may help us understand the past and foresee the future. The Mayan calendar provides an exact schedule for the Cosmic Plan and the unfolding of all things that come into existence."[4]

Ian Xel Lungold

Fig. 14.9
The 12 zodiacal signs in the universal architecture.

The **12** zodiacal signs are positioned inside the circumference of the orange circle of diameter **2,093** tangent to the square of edge length **1,480**, the *gematria value* for 'Christ'*. The **13**th zodiacal sign is the Christ aspect of the human and is located within the heart center.

15. The music of the spheres

The music of the spheres is the universal language of mathematical divine beauty resonating as above so below. Sound is alchemy and alchemy is sound. A construction between circles, squares and further regular polygons contains information of harmonic intervals. Music can be seen as the manifestation of energy spiraling to form.

Fig. 15.1

Illustration from Kepler's Secret of the Universe.

In Kepler's Secret of the Universe, he managed to construct a model showing the distances of the planets from the Sun. The idea was to utilize the radii in the correct sequence by taking the outer sphere of one as the inner sphere of the next. The ratio of the orbital radii of Venus and the Earth was proposed to be related to the ratio of the radii of the inner sphere and the outer sphere of an icosahedron*.

Each of the platonic solids can be enclosed within a sphere touching each vertex or corner and an inner sphere touching the mid point of each face.

The inner and outer spheres have specific ratios regarding their radius, area and volume.

The ancient knowledge of the platonic solids and their connection with the characteristics of the planetary system, seems to have been forgotten or lost. The principle order in the universe naturally emanates from the *Vesica Piscis* generating the regular polygons which form the fundamental Platonic solids in three dimensional form.

Venus is an example offering a surprisingly beautiful geometric pattern of the pentagram as it orbits when viewed from the Earth; The same method applied to other planets in the geocentric view is applicable and presents other beautiful and astonishing mandalas.

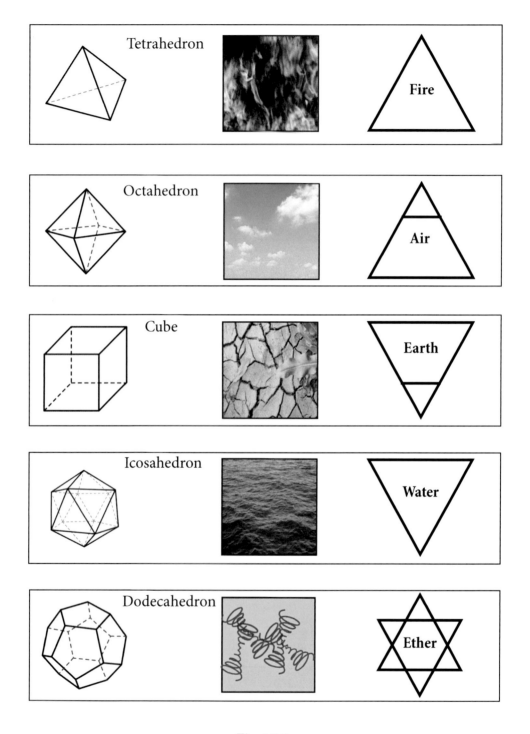

Fig. 15.2
Platonic solids related to their element and alchemical symbol.

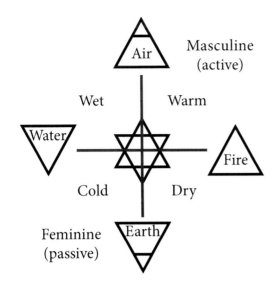

The alchemical symbols are related to the five elements water, air, fire, earth and *ether*.

The Star of David is related to the fifth element *ether*, symbol of balance and unity between the masculine and feminine or Yang and Yin energy.

Fig. 15.3
Alchemical symbols.

If the balance is broken through an unequal force between the two principles, a distortion in the *Seed of Life* pattern appears caused by energy between these two opposing forces losing its coherent flow.

Dr. Masaru Emoto, the famous Japenese scientist demonstrated how thought forms can energetically influenced water as it is frozen into crystal form.

Beautiful and positive thoughts will produce beautiful geometric patterns in the universe. Alternatively, negative thoughts produce distorted geometric patterns.

An experiment with crystallizing water shows this distortion and confirms that consciousness is a vibration and frequency that affects our environment.

Fig. 15.4
Structure and geometry of crystallized water.

The connection between sound and geometry occurs on all scales. Celestial bodies including planets, stars and moons all spin around a center producing different orbital ratios. Pythagoras and Kepler each had the intuitive knowing that music could be seen as geometry and that the interval ratios in a scale directly relate to the orbital ratios of planets.

Fig. 15.5
The cosmic dance of Venus forming a pentagram as viewed from Earth.

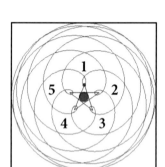

In **8** Earth years Venus orbits the Sun almost **13** times.

During this **8** year cycle Venus gets closest to the Earth about **5** times (**13 – 8 = 5**) and moves each time to a new lobe **3** steps ahead of the last one in the pentagram (**8 - 5 = 3**).

Mars nears the Earth **7** times during a period of **15** Earth years and moves to a new lobe of the heptagram **8** steps ahead of the last one (**15 - 7 = 8**).
Mars orbits the Sun once every **686.989** days. The exact ratio of the orbital period between Mars and Earth is **1.8808:1**, close to the ratio **1.875:1 (120/64)** a C# from D **1:1**. Mars' musical note is almost a C# at **135** Hz in relation to D at **72** Hz.

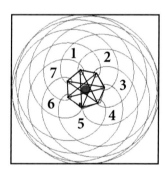

Fig. 15.6
The cosmic dance of Mars forming a heptagram as viewed from Earth.

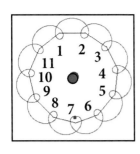

Fig. 15.
The cosmic dance of
*Jupiter forming a hendecagon
(11-gon) as viewed from Earth.*

Jupiter nears the Earth every **11.861** Earth years and moves to a new lobe of the hendecagon (**11**-gon) one step ahead of the last.

Jupiter orbits the Sun once every **4,332.589** days. The exact ratio of the orbital period is **11.861:1** close to the ratio **12:1** a perfect fifth A from D. Jupiter's musical note is about **864** Hz reflecting the Sun's diameter in miles.

Mercury nears the Earth almost **3** times during a period of **88** Earth days and moves to a new lobe of the triangle one step ahead of the last.

Mercury orbits the Sun once every **87.96934** days. The exact ratio of the orbital period is **0.24:1** close to the ratio **0.25:1**, a D. Mercury's musical note is **18** Hz in relation to D at **72** Hz.

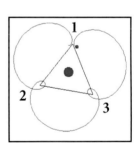

Fig. 15.8
*The cosmic dance of Mercury
forming a triangle
as viewed from Earth.*

"Listen within yourself and look into the infinitude of Space and Time. There can be heard the songs of the Constellations, the voices of the Numbers, and the harmonies of the Spheres."

Hermes Trismegistus

When Earth completes **8** revolutions in relation to the sun, Venus completes **13** revolutions. The ratio between the revolutions of Venus and Earth is **13:8** corresponding to the musical note **117 Hz** from a Divine D **72 Hz**. The harmonic number **117** encodes the dimensions of the Great Pyramid with **7** being the height and **11** being the base leg (Fig 1.10).

Earth and Venus respectively orbit the Sun once every **365.256** and **224.701** days. The exact ratio of their orbital periods is **1.6255:1** close to **13:8** shown in equation (24). **8** and **13** are the **8**[th] and **9**[th] numbers appearing in the *Fibonacci* sequence, creating the *Fibonacci Spiral* (Fig 4.1).

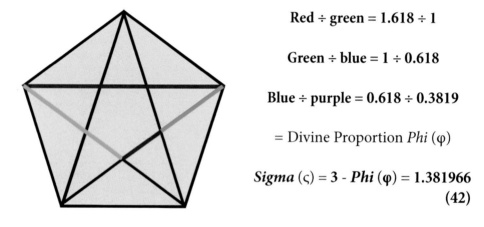

$$\textbf{Red} \div \textbf{green} = \textbf{1.618} \div \textbf{1}$$

$$\textbf{Green} \div \textbf{blue} = \textbf{1} \div \textbf{0.618}$$

$$\textbf{Blue} \div \textbf{purple} = \textbf{0.618} \div \textbf{0.3819}$$

$$= \text{Divine Proportion } \textit{Phi } (\varphi)$$

$$\textit{Sigma } (\varsigma) = \textbf{3 - } \textit{Phi } (\varphi) = \textbf{1.381966}$$
$$(42)$$

Fig. 15.9
Orbital ratio between Venus and Earth in the pentagram.

The distances of Earth and Venus from the Sun are respectively **93,312,000** and **67,495,482** miles. The orbital ratio of **1.38249** between Venus and Earth approximates to *Sigma* (ς) with a value of **1.381966**. This factor also arises naturally by subtracting *phi* (ϕ) from **1**, shown in equation (43).

$$\textbf{1} \div \textbf{1.61803399} = \textbf{0.61803399} \qquad (43)$$
$$\textbf{1 - 0.61803399} = \textbf{0.381966}$$

The value Sigma (ς) **1.381966** is obtained from the calculation **3** minus *Phi* (φ) **1.618** (**3 - 1.61803399**).

> *"There is geometry in the humming of the strings. There is music in the spacing of the spheres."*   **Pythagoras**

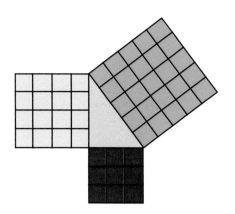

The Pythagorean triangle with sides 3 - 4 - 5 is an important triangle encoding a remarkable property of the cube **6 x 6 x 6** or *Hypercube 216* ($3^3 + 4^3 + 5^3 = 6^3$).

Hypercube 216 is a perfect cube as its volume of **216** is the total sum of the volume of the three cubes of edge length **3**, **4** and **5** each.

Fig. 15.10
The Pythagorean Triangle 3 - 4 - 5

$$3^3 + 4^3 + 5^3 = 6^3 = 216 \qquad (44)$$

> *"Numbers have a way of taking a man by the hand and leading him down the path of reason."*
>
> **Pythagoras**

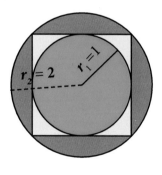

Interval ratios between musical notes can be interpreted through the spiral or through the geometric construction between a circle and the regular polygons.

Fig. 15.11
The octave in geometry.

Unison 1:1 Area $A_1 = \pi r_1^2$ (blue)

Octave 2:1 Area $A_2 = \pi r_2^2$ (green)

$r_2 = \sqrt{2}\, r_1$ then $A_2 = 2\, A_1$ (45)

The unison **1:1** can be interpreted as the area of the blue circle of radius 1. The green circle is twice the area of the blue circle and represents the octave **2:1**. The yellow square has a diagonal of $2\sqrt{2}$.

A blue circle of radius **1** inscribed inside the orange hexagon produces the perfect fourth **4:3**. The yellow circle surrounding the hexagon has a radius equal to **2÷√3**.

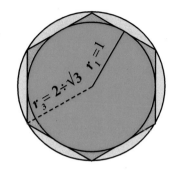

Unison **1:1** Area $A_1 = \pi\, r_1^{\,2}$(blue)

Perfect fourth **4:1** Area $A_3 = \pi\, r_3^{\,2}$(yellow)

$r_3 = 2 \div \sqrt{3}\ r_1$ then $A_3 = 4 \div 3\ A_1$ **(46)**

Fig. 15.12
The Perfect Fourth
in geometry.

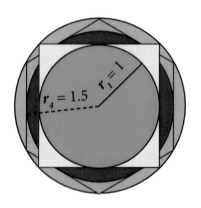

An interval can arise out of different combinations between the regular polygons, such as the perfect fifth **3:2** being the combination of the yellow square and orange hexagon through the operation **2:1** divided by **4:3**.

Perfect fifth **1.5:1** Area $A_4 = \pi\, r_4^{\,2}$

$r_4 = r_2 \div r_3 = \sqrt{(3 \div 2)}\ r_1$ (purple)

$A_4 = A_2 \div A_3 = (3 \div 2)\, A_1$ **(47)**

Fig. 15.13
The Perfect Fifth
in geometry.

This method shows how music can be interpreted geometrically and suggests that everything made of geometric shapes can also be seen as sound waves. It is worth remembering that geometric patterns can be transformed through thought forms or intent. Therefore a thought form itself is a sound wave vibrating at a frequency expressing a geometric pattern.

16. The Fine Structure Constant

The fine-structure constant is considered as the most mysterious number in physics. Below are some quotations.

> *"There is a most profound and beautiful question associated with the observed coupling constant, e – the amplitude for a real electron to emit or absorb a real photon. It is a simple number that has been experimentally determined to be close to 0.08542455. (My physicist friends won't recognize this number, because they like to remember it as the inverse of its square: about 137.03597 with about an uncertainty of about 2 in the last decimal place. It has been a mystery ever since it was discovered more than fifty years ago, and all good theoretical physicists put this number up on their wall and worry about it.) Immediately you would like to know where this number for a coupling comes from: is it related to π or perhaps to the base of natural logarithms? Nobody knows. It's one of the greatest damn mysteries of physics: a magic number that comes to us with no understanding by man. You might say the "hand of God" wrote that number, and "we don't know how He pushed his pencil." We know what kind of a dance to do experimentally to measure this number very accurately, but we don't know what kind of dance to do on the computer to make this number come out, without putting it in secretly!"* [1]
>
> **Richard Feynman**

> *"If alpha [the fine structure constant] were bigger than it really is, we should not be able to distinguish matter from ether [the vacuum, nothingness], and our task to disentangle the natural laws would be hopelessly difficult. The fact however that alpha has just its value 1/137 is certainly no chance but itself a law of nature. It is clear that the explanation of this number must be the central problem of natural philosophy."* [2]
>
> **Max Born, Arthur I. Miller**

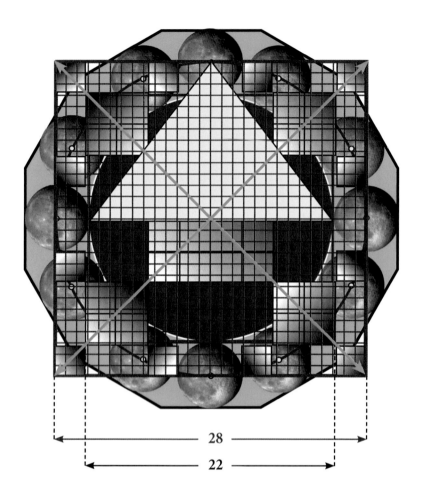

28

22

Fig. 16.1
A **28 x 28** *grid in the Etheric Particle.*

The *fine structure constant Alpha* (α) can be calculated through the geometric construct of the *Etheric Particle.*

A **28 x 28** grid of square units shown in red superimposed on the *Etheric Particle* has an area equal to **784**.

There are **288** sparkles of light in the Windmill Hill crop circle. **784** divided by **288** is approximately **2.72**, the megalithic yard in feet, suggesting the megalithic builders were working with the *ether.*

Interestingly **784** is the sum of the volumes of cubes with an edge length from one to seven.

$$1^3 + 2^3 + 3^3 + 4^3 + 5^3 + 6^3 + 7^3 = 28^2 = 784 \tag{48}$$

There is a relationship between the *fine structure constant Alpha* (α), *the Light Body Constant Delta* (δ), *Pi* (π) and the *Golden Ratio Phi* (φ) shown in equation (49).

$$784\,\alpha = \delta + 2 \quad \text{and} \quad \delta\,\pi = (4\,\delta \div \sqrt{\varphi}) \approx 784 \div 67 \tag{49}$$

Equation (49) can be rewritten as equation (50).

$$784\,[(\,\alpha - 1 \div (67\,\pi)] = 2 \tag{50}$$

After simplification, (50) becomes (51).

$$\alpha = 2 \div 784 + \sqrt{\varphi} \div 268 \tag{51}$$

The *fine structure constant Alpha* (α) can be written as the sum of two terms incorporating the dimensions of the Great Pyramid, with a base leg of **2** and a height of $\sqrt{\varphi}$ (Fig 1.12). Light manifests from the centre of the base of the Great Pyramid where the blue diagonal lines cross in Figure 16.1.

- **2 ÷ 784** is the amplitude of the etheric force across the base of the Pyramid.
- $\sqrt{\varphi} \div 268$ is the amplitude of the etheric force applied vertically inside the Pyramid.
- *The fine structure constant Alpha* (α) represents the sum of the two above etheric forces directed half way up the slope sides of the Pyramid. Creative energy can be viewed as a fractal of squares expanding through the diagonals toward the corners (*Fractal 44*).
- **784 ÷ 268** is approximately equal to the side of a square *E* in the light body of *Vitruvian Man* (Fig 12.7).

The amplitude of the etheric forced applied vertically can be further expressed in equation below.

$$\sqrt{\varphi} \div 268 \approx 7 \div 1{,}474.82 \tag{52}$$
$$\approx [7\,(12\sqrt{2})] \div 25{,}028.52$$
$$\approx (84\sqrt{2}) \div 25{,}028.52$$

1,474.82 is approximately equal to **1,480** the *gematria value* for 'Christ'* and **25,028.52** is approximately equal to **25,000** the edge length of the gifted land in reeds (Chapter 14).

---

* *See Gematria*   139

The constant *Alpha* (α) is approximately equal to the inverse ratio of **137** and can be calculated with half the area of a face of *Hypercube 216* equal to **5,184** (Fig 5.3) and the number **666** (equation 53).

288 represents luminic energy of the *Etheric Particle* (Fig 5.5) and **37** is the geometric and numerical foundation of light (Fig 13.8 and equation 27).

$$10^{\omega} \div 666^2 = 137.036 \tag{53}$$

with $\omega = 5,184 \div 666 = 216 \div 27.75 = 82,944 \div 10,656 = 288 \div 37$

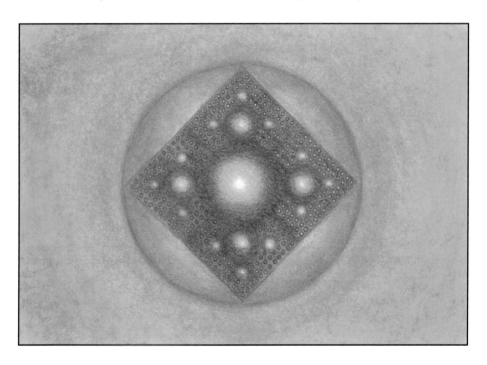

Fig. 16.2
Artistic expression of the Windmill Hill crop circle (Fig 2.12).

Figure 16.2 shows an artist's impression of the Windmill Hill crop circle with added circles expressing Pyramid Energy. One quadrant of the square contains **72** feminine circles.

Omega (ω) can be expressed as **5,184** divided by **666,** and **288** the total number of circles in the Windmill Hill crop circle, divided by the prime number **37.** The result is approximately **7.783** which can be written as **216** divided by **27.75,** referring to **216** spins of *Hypercube 216* during a period of **27.75** lunar days.

The pathway of light can be geometrically interpreted as a line between two points. For example, in a triangle, there are three possible pathways between the three points. For a square there are four edges and two diagonals for light to travel.

Fig. 16.3
Artistic expression of the West Kennet crop circle (Fig 2.13).

One quadrant of the square contains **39** masculine circles.

Light has **666** possible pathways in a set of **37** energetic points (triangular number **36**). Light has **5,151** possible pathways in a set of **102** *Zero Energy Points*. **5,151** added to **33** brings **5,184** a numerical key of *Hypercube 216*.

In one quadrant of the *Geometric Key*, the difference between the number of feminine circles (purple) and masculine circles (yellow) is **33** (**72 - 39 = 33**), a numerical key of the *Etheric Particle* on scale *A* (Fig 8.6).

The Hebrew word '*Kabbala*'* (קבלה) which means 'receiving' has a *gematria value* of **137**.

From a *Zero Energy Point* a certain number of photons are emitted when *Hypercube 216* spins. It can be viewed as a photon flux crossing the surface of the yellow square of edge length **666**.

← **666** →

Fig. 16.4
The photon flux.

Key B, Cornerstone
666 of the *universal architecture.*
(Fig. 10.2)

Christ Sphere

In Equation (53) the number of photons is **10** to the power *Omega* (ω) (**$10^{ω}$**). The average number of photons per square of edge length **666** is **137.036**.

The circumference of the green circle *P* squared (P^2) in the light body of *Vitruvian Man* (Fig 12.7) is approximately equal to **137.02**.

Fine structure constant Alpha (α) $$P^2 = (\delta \pi)^2 \approx 137.02 \approx 1 \div \alpha \quad (54)$$

Each red point is a *Zero Energy Point* behaving like a mini torus producing a fractal of **288** sparkles of light. The total number of sparkles of light is **10,656** which is **288** multiplied by **37**.

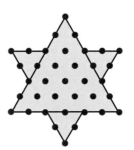

Fig. 16.5
The Star of David with 37 Zero Energy Points.

28 dots in each triangle of **7** rows.

Omega (ω) is the equivalent mass of the *Etheric Particle* **82,944** divided by **10,656** (equation 3). The harmonic number **10,656** is the sum of the *gematria values* for the **12** names of Jesus' disciples.

Peter* πετρος, Andrew Ανδρεας, James Ιακωβος, John Ιωαννης, Philip Φιλιππος, Nathanael Ναθαναηλ, Levi (Matthew) Λευι, Thomas Θωμας, James (Son of Alpheus) Ιακωβος Αλφαιου, Lebbaeus Λεββαιος, Simon Σιμων ο καναναιος, Judas Ιουδας[3].

The understanding of the *fine structure constant* will lead to a great understanding of spiral energy.

The eccentric outwardly expanding Yang spiral (centrifugence) encourages decomposition in nature, breakdown, whereas a concentric inward Yin spiral builds and energizes (centripetence).

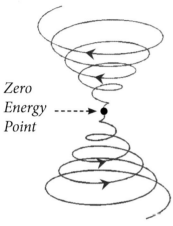

Zero
Energy - - - - ->
Point

Fig. 16.6
*The two natural modes of
opposite spiral motions.*

Fig. 16.7
*Spiral on a stone found on
the Isle of Man.*

Fig. 16.8
Spirals carved into stone at the entrance of Newgrange, Ireland.

When water drains through a plug, an upward spiral motion can be observed seemingly in opposition to gravity (waves in blue). The waves traveling upward are supported by the etheric forces suggesting the possibility of levitation (waves in red).

Fig. 16.9
Water Vortex.

Gravity
Forces

Waves
travelling
downward

The stone sphere of
Costa Rica, **15** tons.

The Sun Gate in Tihuanaco,
Bolivia, **10** tons.

Half quarried stone at Baalbek,
1,650 - 1820 tons.

Fig. 16.10
*Enormous stone structures
from the ancient world.*

Impossible achievements considering
our present state of technology.

Fig 17.1
The Flammarion: Universum

The *Firmament* can be conceptualized as a wall, beyond which lies a different reality from this third dimensional experience. The *ether* is a force connecting the inside to the outside of the firmament and the edge of the third dimension. The *Flammarion* is a wood engraving by an unknown artist, depicting a medieval cosmology with a flat earth bounded by a firmament. The sun and moon orbit within a firmament encrusted with stars. Beyond the veil lies a strange world with wheels reminiscent of *Vedic* spaceships. The three dimensional world of earth, air, fire and water is contrasted with the etheric realm.

> *"Man is a microcosm, or a little world, because he is an extract from all the stars and planets of the whole firmament, from the earth and the elements; and so he is their quintessence."* **Paracelsus**

Fig 17.2
Firmament 33 and the Etheric Particle.

Inside wall **28**

Firmament and outside wall **33**

Looking at Figure 17.2 the edge of the purple square defines *Firmament 33* and the outside wall of the *New Jerusalem*. The twelve white squares of *Fractal 44* correlate with the **12** moons around Earth, the **12** zodiacal signs and the camp of the **12** tribes of Israel (Figs 2.8, 2.10 and 2.11).

There is a different experience of reality beyond the firmament. The structure of the universe changes, which means the universe is non-isotropic. An isotropic universe means that the structure of the universe is the same in all directions. If the Earth is considered as being in the centre of the cosmos, this means the universe cannot be homogeneous. A homogeneous universe is defined as there being no preferred observation point in the universe. The universe is non-uniform which means neither isotropic or homogeneous.

146

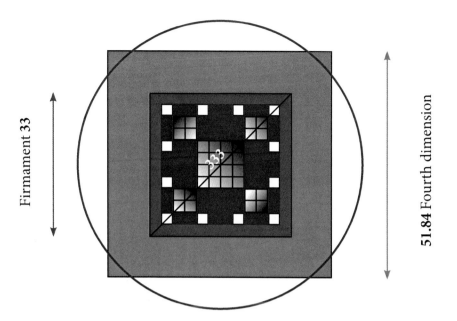

Fig 17.3
Squaring the circle beyond Firmament 33.

Beyond *Firmament* **33**, reality becomes a fourth dimensional experience contained within the orange square. The edge length of this square is approximately **51.84**, the edge length of *Cornerstone 666* (Fig 8.7) and the slope angle of the Great Pyramid in degrees.

In three dimensions, the firmament (purple square) can be seen as a cube contained within a bigger cube (orange square) forming the *Tesseract,* a cube in the fourth dimension.

Fig. 17.4
The matryoshka.

The matryoshka or nested doll principle describes the nature of the universe as an unfolding three dimensional geometry.

In ancient cosmology Earth is a geometric structure rather than a round ball floating in endless space and was regarded as flat, rectangular or square and bounded by four walls or a toroidal shape with a curvature in the centre creating a mound, mountain or tree. Ancient knowledge has been preserved in these art works.

Fig. 17.5
*Nun the primeval waters
lifting the boat.*

In Mesopotamia, Israel and Ancient Egypt the world was portrayed as a flat disk floating on water beneath an arched firmament separating it from the heavens. In Ancient Egypt they called the primeval oceans *Nun or the abyss*, a circular or disk-shaped body of water from where the lotus bestowed a sacred mound.

In the Egyptian Coffin Texts, the Earth was surrounded by the primeval waters or *Nun* and was referred to as *nbwt* meaning dry lands or islands. Earth was also represented as a Lotus floating on the primeval waters.

The spherical model first appears during Pythagoras' time in the 6th century. Earlier the same century around 550 AD, a Greek sailor named Cosmas Indicopleustes wrote a volume of books advancing the idea that the world is flat and the heavens form the shape of a box with a curved lid.

In Figure 17.6, Cosmas Indicopleustes created one of the oldest world maps showing the floor of a tabernacle-shaped universe and a rectangular landmass in the middle of the World Ocean. A tabernacle shaped universe is one possible geometric shape for Earth floating on Nun, the primeval oceans.

In the biblical scripture Ezekiel described a gifted land of **25,000** reeds representing the universe as a cube container of edge length **25,000** units. Ezekiel and Cosmas Indicopleustes were both conveying Earth and the universe in geometric terms.

Keys

A. Roman Gulf from East
B. Arabian Gulf from South
C. Persian Gulf from West
D. Caspian sea from North

Sun path and seasons

E. Winter night
F. Equinox
G. Summer night

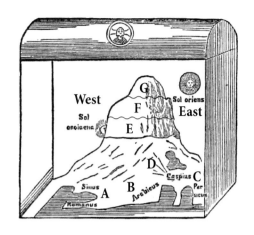

Fig. 17.6
The World according to Cosmas Indicopleustes.

> "But the earth is not supported upon itself, but is set upon the realm of the waters, while this again is kept in its place, being bound fast at the center of the universe."[2]
> **Athanasius**

Fig. 17.7
Painting of Mount Meru from the Samghayanarayana.

Ancient Indian, Hindu, Jain and Buddhist cosmology believed that the Earth is a disc bounded by mountains on which the continents are set as small islands.

They are grouped around a central mountain known as Mount Meru, surrounded by an outer ocean. On Mount Meru, there are **432** Buddha statues and **72** dome shaped shrines known as stupas.

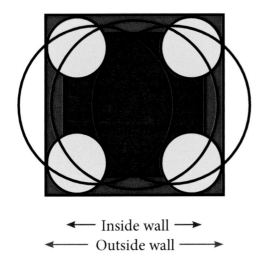

Fig. 17.8

A 13th century manuscript of the Apocalypse from the British Museum depicting the New Jerusalem[1].

According to Stirling in his book *The Canon*[2] the circumference of each corner circle is **144** and the circumferences of the circles forming the *Vesica Piscis* in the centre is nearly **360**.

← Inside wall →

← Outside wall →

According to Marke Pawson in his book *Gematria*, the four circles on each corner represent the four fundamental interactive forces of electromagnetism, gravity, strong and weak nuclear. Ezekiel described four creatures possibly representing the four creative energies of spirit or the four corner signs of the Zodiac, Taurus, Leo, Scorpio, and Aquarius[3] shown on the front cover of this book.

Fig. 17.9
An alternative version of the New Jerusalem.

From the data listed in Figure 8.6, the area inside the wall of the *New Jerusalem* is shown in red and the area contained by the *Firmament* is shown in purple, almost tangent to the circles creating the *Vesica Piscis*.

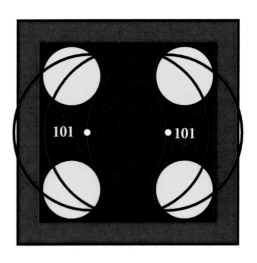

In my opinion, the tabernacle is the *holiest structure* representing the emanation of the fifth force emerging from the centre of the circles forming the *Vesica Piscis*. The position of the *most holy place* of the Temple of Solomon sits on a **101** *Zero Energy Point* gateway, depicted in Figures 17.9, 17.10 and 17.11.

The corners of the **4 x 4** grid in the centre touch the *Vesica Piscis* and the two black circles of circumference **360** touch the edges of the **12**-sided green dodecagon.

The circumference of the black circle in the centre is **384**, the double of **192**.

Golden Spirals emanate from the green squares which represent **101** *Zero Energy Points* from a cube of **20** cubits width, length and breadth.

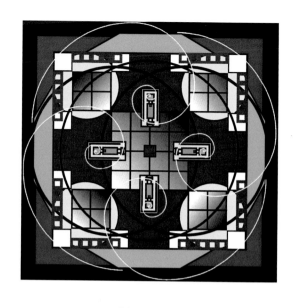

This cube represents the sanctuary of the Holy Temple containing the Ark of Covenant*.

Fig. 17.10
Temple of Solomon and Fractal 44 superimposed on the New Jerusalem.

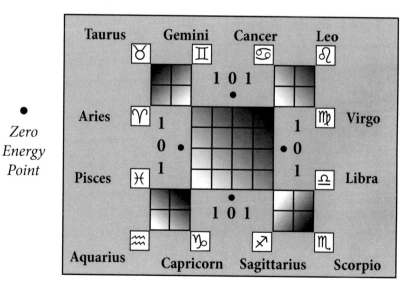

Fig. 17.11
The 12 single squares hold the 12 zodiacal signs.

The number **20** connects the *fine structure constant Alpha* (α) with the *Golden Ratio Phi* (φ) **1.618** in equation (55).

$$20\,\varphi^4 \approx 137.082 \approx 1 \div Alpha\ (\alpha) \tag{55}$$

In the Mayan Calendar system the number **20** is the multiplicative factor for building the Temple of Kukulkan (Fig 14.3).

The edge length of the sanctuary is **34.56** feet or **20 x 1.728** feet (the Egyptian cubit Fig 11.1). **3,456** is the *gematria value* for 'City of my God'* (της πολεως Θεου μου[4]). The product of **3, 4, 5,** and **6** is **360**, the circumference of each black circle forming the *Vesica Piscis* (Fig 17.8). The *gematria value* for 'Scarlet'* (שני[5]) and for 'Sheen Nun Yod'* (שני[6]) is **360**. 'Sheen Nun Yod' means 'twinned', suggesting that the Scarlet consists of two strands. These two strands emanate from the green squares representing the sanctuary of the Holy Temple of Solomon and the two opposing *Golden Spirals* of Yin and Yang energy.

There are twelve precious stones (gems) associated with the twelve foundation stones of the *Etheric Particle* with a total *gematria value*[7] of **12,442**. Each tribe of Israel is associated to a foundation stone in New Jerusalem.

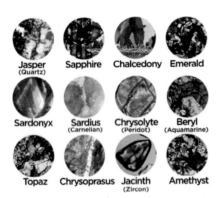

Jasper (Quartz)   Sapphire   Chalcedony   Emerald

Sardonyx   Sardius (Carnelian)   Chrysolyte (Peridot)   Beryl (Aquamarine)

Topaz   Chrysoprasus   Jacinth (Zircon)   Amethyst

Fig. 17.12
New Jerusalem Gemstones
of Revelation 21:18-20.

The number **12,442** refers to **124,416** with one less decimal point, a numerical key of *Hypercube 216* (**10,368 x 12**). The reed of **6** greater cubits in feet is also **12.4416** (Chap 12, p 108). Equation (56) relates **360** to **12,442** and **34.56**.

$$12,442 \div 34.56 \approx 360 \qquad 124,416 \div 34.56 = 3,600 = 60^2 \tag{56}$$

The twelve precious stones work together as a divine system producing opposing twinned waves (Fig 16.6).

Fig. 17.13
The New Jerusalem, Temple of Solomon and Etheric Particle.

The *fine structure constant Alpha* (α) characterizes the etheric force, the fire of the Great Spirit coming from the centre of the black circles forming the *Vesica Piscis* and creating the four fundamental forces through the yellow circles. These four forces, Electromagnetism, Gravity, Strong and Weak nuclear forces are directed along the blue diagonal lines toward the corners of *Fractal 44*. This important interaction defines a connected universe through the unification of Matter and Spirit.

The Ark of the Covenant has a width and length of **1.5** cubits (**1.5 x 1.728 = 2.592 ft**) and a height of **2.5** cubits (**2.5 x 1.728 = 4.32 ft**).

2.592 is a ten thousandth of **25,920,** a fractal of the period of precession of the equinoxes in years and one hundredth of **259.2,** a fractal of a Mayan year in days. **4.32** leads to **432,** the *gematria value* for 'Bethlehem'* (Βηθλεεμ), 'Gethsemane' (Γεθσημανι), 'Jerusalem' (ירושלם), 'All Nations' (כלגוים) by multiplication of each letter.[8]

The following equation gives strong evidence for a true value of *Pi* (π) of **3.1446055*** in relation to the numbers **2.592, 10.368** and the square root of *Phi* (√φ).

$$2.592 \; \pi \; \sqrt{\varphi} = 10.368 \tag{57}$$

The Ark is an important technological artefact matching the dimensions of the Coffer in the King's Chamber of the Great Pyramid. The Ark may have been placed inside the Coffer to harness etheric energy or to produce free energy directly from the interaction between earth and sky, Yin and Yang. The Great Pyramid is a meeting and accumulation point of the natural balance of life.

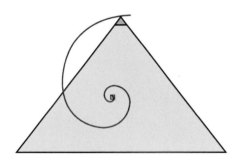

The Ark may act as an accumulator of etheric energy inside the Coffer.

This energy is then conducted through a *Golden Spiral* to the capstone above magnifying the energy coming from inside and creating a powerful etheric energy field around the pyramid.

Fig. 17.14
The Ark of Covenant and the Great Pyramid.

The Coffer in the King's chamber is a gateway for etheric creative energy, a **101** *Zero Energy Point* of the *Etheric Particle.*

The volume of the Ark matches the volume of the Coffer (**31.104** inches **x** **31.104** inches **x** **51.84** inches).

Fig. 17.15
The Coffer in the King's chamber.

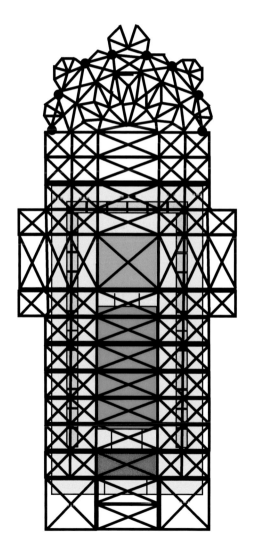

31,104 divided by **3** is **10,368**, the surface area of a face of *Hypercube 216.*
51.84 is one hundredth of one Mayan Baktun **5,184** in years and the slope angle of the Great Pyramid.

Fig. 17.16
Floor plan of Chartres Cathedral superimposed on the Temple of Solomon.

The crossing point on the ground plan matches the sanctuary of the Holy Temple of Solomon, the green square*. The crossing point is also a **101** *Zero Energy Point* from *Fractal 44.*

Earth

Fig. 18.1
The Etheric Particle.

The *Etheric Particle* holds important numerical keys studied in this book and there are undoubtedly more to discover. This is the realm of numbers, the language of the universe. All is number.

This book urges musicians to tune their instrument at **432** Hz. The reason is that **432** is an important numerical key of the *Etheric Particle*. Creative energy or life force emanates everywhere from all things in the Universe. This particle connects all things together through the Divine manifestation of *Golden Spirals* or Pyramid Energy as the unification of matter and spirit, including the four fundamental interactions Electromagnetism, Gravity, Strong and Weak nuclear forces.

The twelve foundation stones are the twelve moons around Earth each encoding the number **360**. There are **360** degrees in a circle and each moon represents a circle bringing a total of **4,320** degrees (**360 x 12**). **4,320** divided by the *Golden Ratio Phi* (φ) power to 15 (φ^{15}) is approximately **3.168**, *gematria value* for Lord Jesus-Christ* (*Κυριος ιησουσ χριστος*).

The *Golden Ratio Phi* (φ) to the power of **15** (φ^{15}) is **1,364**. This number naturally encodes some information about the Moon. There are **364** days in a lunar year. Eleven octaves below of **1,364**, which means **1,364** divided by **2,048** is approximately equal to **0.666**, **666** a number of Beauty representing the manifestation of the Divine Blueprint.

Musicians on your chords, get ready to bring forward the revolution of numbers by tuning your instrument at **432** Hz in order to resonate with the *ether*. The speed of light in a vacuum is **432** squared in miles per second, **186,624**, the **8**[th] octave above F# at **729** Hz.

The speed of sound through granite is **12,960** ft per second (**432 x 3**) and is five octaves above G# at **405** Hz.

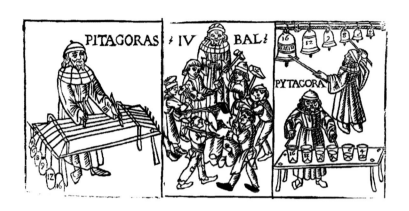

" *Music is a universal language, as are numbers. The two go hand in hand. Beautifully divisible numbers create our harmonic intervals when we tune the note A to 432Hz. This brings our note D to 144Hz. With modern concert pitch these numbers appear as 146.8Hz and 440Hz and no longer mirror the fractal growth of the numbers one and nine creating the Pythagorean harmonic system. Tuning to 432Hz brings music into harmonic alignment with the numerical universe from where all things originate. A wider sound of richer overtones can be experienced along with relaxed feelings which come from connection to source. Equal temperament or equal ratios between notes is another obstacle to experiencing perfect harmony and perfect alignment. We have become accustomed to hearing major thirds and sevenths almost unbearably high in relation to their true value. When particular attention is paid to tuning each note to its correct harmonic position crystal chords ring out mirroring the numerical masterpiece of nature. In finer times J.S. Bach demonstrated this with his suite for the 'Well-Tempered Clavier'. Go forth and crystallise!* "

Michael Tyack, Musician

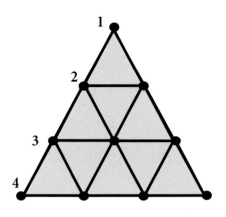

Fig. 18.2
Music and the Tetractys.

The *Tetractys* is said to be the fundamental geometry on which the Pythagorean musical system was based

The rows can be read as the ratio of **4:3** (perfect fourth), **3:2** (perfect fifth), **2:1** (octave), and the unison itself **1:1**.

These interval ratios formed the basic intervals of Pythagorean scales, which defined the Pythagorean musical system. The idea was that the ratios were made of the numbers **1, 2, 3, 4, 5** and that there were five planets moving with similar ratios.

The *Tetractys*, an equilateral triangle can be made of **9** smaller equilateral triangles or **9** consciousness units within the *Flower of Life*.

The *Flower of Life* is made of a multiple of consciousness units seen as equilateral triangles which means an infinite matrix of *Tetractys*. This beautiful geometric pattern can also be viewed as a grid of standing wave interferences producing geometry governed by numbers and music. Some numbers are remarkable in the construction of perfect polygons such as **108** the interior angle of a pentagon producing the musical note A in Hertz (Fig 7.5).

Fig. 18.3
The Tetractys within the Flower of Life.

Many of the harmonic numbers discussed in this book can be interpreted as musical notes based on a D scale from **9** Hz. Below is a list of numbers showing their musical and geometric equivalents.

Figure 18.4 lists some of the numbers, all of root **9**. These numbers are related to the Divine proportion *Phi* (φ) **1.618** through the operation cosine and sine (Fig 7.7).

In the list below, *H216 = Hypercube 216.*

Fig. 18.4
Numbers of root **9**

126	162	234	306	324
342	378	468	486	504
576	612	648	684	702
738	918	936	972	

72   D 72 circles for one quadrant of the Windmill Hill crop circle (Fig 5.2).

72√2   Close to a G# at **101.25** Hz, edge length of *H216* (Fig 5.3).

108   A Interior angle of a pentagon (Fig 7.5).

126   C see Figure 18.4 above.

135   C# Interior angle of an octagon (Fig 7.7).

144   D Diagonal line of a face of *H216* (Fig 5.3).

153   E^b The miraculous catch of fish by Jesus in the Bible scripture (John 21:1–14).

162   Octave above E at **81** Hz. Equation (2) of *H216* (Fig 5.3).

180   Octave above F# at **90** Hz. Degrees in a semi circle or square.

192   A Pythagorean G from C at **64** Hz. Light body in four dimensions (Fig 12.7).

216   Three octaves above A at **27** Hz. Total number of single cubes in *H216* (Fig 5.3).

234   Octave above B^b at **117** Hz (Fig 18.4).

252   Two octaves above C at **63** Hz. *Gematria value* for Light (המאור).

270   Octave above C# at **135** Hz. From the equation of standing wave interferences (Fig 7.17).

288   Octave above D at **144** Hz. Luminic energy of the *Etheric Particle* (Fig 5.4).

306   Octave above E^b at **153** Hz (Fig 18.4).

324   Two octaves above E at **81** Hz (Fig 18.4).

342   Octave above F at **117** Hz (Fig 18.4).

351   Harmonic F#, energy frequency voltage of *H216*.

360   Two octaves above F# at **90** Hz, total degrees in a circle or square.

378   Octave above G at **189** Hz, 21st harmonic from D at **9** Hz (Fig 18.4).

384   Octave above **192** Hz, a Pythagorean G from C at **64** Hz. Equivalent mass of a single cube inside *H216*.

159

432	Four octaves above A at **27** Hz. Cosmic code of the *Tetractys* (Fig 1.1).
468	Two octaves above B^b at **117** Hz (Fig 18.4).
486	Octave above B at **243** Hz (Fig 18.4).
504	Three octaves above C at **63** Hz (Fig 18.4).
576	Six octaves above D at **9** Hz (Fig 18.4).
612	Two octaves above E^b at **153** Hz (Fig 18.4).
648	Three octaves above E at **81** Hz (Fig 18.4).
684	Two octaves above F at **171** Hz (Fig 18.4).
702	Octave above **351** Hz, harmonic F#. A quarter of **2,808**, energy frequency voltage of the *Etheric Particle* (Chapter 16).
720	Three octaves above F# at **90** Hz. The sum of the interior angles of the Tetrahedron (Fig 1.3).
756	Two octaves above G at **189** Hz (Fig 18.4).
864	Five octaves above A at **27** Hz. One thousandth of the Sun's diameter in miles.
918	Octave above B^b at **459** Hz. See Figure 18.4.
936	Three octaves above B^b at **117** Hz. See Figure 18.4.
972	Two octaves above B at **243** Hz. See Figure 18.4.
1,008	Four octaves above C at **63** Hz, one tenth of the Earth and moon's diameter added together in miles.
1,080	Three octaves above C# at **135** Hz, Half Moon's diameter in miles.
1,296	Four octaves above E at **81** Hz, the volume of a cube of edge length **6** in four dimensions (Fig 5.4).
1,440	Four octaves above F# at **90** Hz, **24** hours in minutes.
1,728	Six octaves above A at **27** Hz, one thousandth of the Egyptian cubit in feet (Fig 11.1).
2,160	Four octaves above C# at **135** Hz, Moon's diameter in miles.
2,808	Three octaves above **351** Hz, harmonic F#, energy frequency voltage of *H216* (Chapter 5).
3,072	Four octaves above **192** Hz, a Pythagorean G from C at **64** Hz.
3,240	Three octaves above G# at **405** Hz, the sum of the interior angles of a honeycomb cell (On the right of Fig 1.9).
4,320	Five octaves above C# at **135** Hz, the sum of the interior angles of the rhombic dodecahedron (On the left of Fig 1.9).
5,184	Six octaves above E at **81** Hz, the slope angle of the Great Pyramid in degrees is one hundredth of **5,184** (Fig 1.14).
6,480	Four octaves above G# at **405** Hz, the sum of the interior angles of a dodecahedron (Fig 1.8).

10,368	Seven octaves above E at **81** Hz, the surface area of a face of *H216* in units (Fig 5.3).
12,096	Six octaves above G at **189** Hz, 21st harmonic from D at **9** Hz. **12 x 12** grid in miles (Fig 8.5).
15,552	Six octave above B at **243** Hz, three Mayan baktuns of **5,184** years (Fig 14.1).
20,736	Eight octaves above E at **81** Hz, the Egyptian cubit in inches is one thousandth of **20,736**. Two faces of *H216* has a surface area equal to **20,736** (Fig 5.3).
24,576	Six octaves above **192** Hz, a Pythagorean G from C at **64** Hz. Equivalent mass of *Hypercube* **64** (Fig 5.7).
25,920	Six octaves above G# **405** Hz, the complete precession of the equinoxes in years (Fig 14.1).
31,680	55th harmonic of D at **9** Hz, the perimeter of the square surrounding the Earth in miles (Fig 9.6).
82,944	Ten octaves above E at **81** Hz, volume of a single cube inside *H216* in four dimensions (Fig 5.3).
124,416	Eight octaves above B at **486** Hz, the greater cubit is a ten thousandth of **124,416** (Chapter 11).
165,888	Ten octaves above E at **81** Hz, age of the universe in billions of years in the Mayan Calendar (Fig 14.4) or Sumerian cubit in feet (Chapter 11).
186,624	Eight octaves above F# at **729** Hz. Speed of light in miles/sec.

19. The Rainbow Principle

The *Rainbow Principle* reveals that the architects of the ancient Pyramids of Egypt were completely aware of their function in relation to sunlight and water.

When light enters a water droplet, it bends as it reduces speed and transits from air to water. The light reflects off the inside of the droplet, separating it into its component wavelengths, and colours. As light exits the droplet, it produces a rainbow.

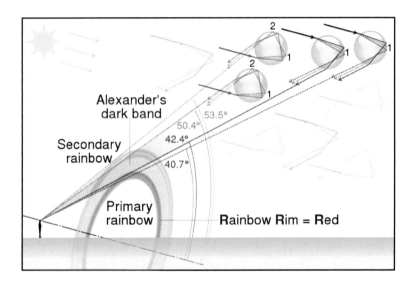

Fig. 19.1
Physics of a primary and secondary rainbow and Alexander's dark band

The three main Pyramids of Giza in Cairo, Egypt, have sloped angles, which match the angles necessary to observe a primary rainbow (**40-42 degrees within our vision**) and a secondary rainbow (**50-53 degrees within our vision**).

Below is a table presenting the sloped angles of the three main Pyramids of Giza: Cheops, the Greatest Pyramid, Khafre, the second-tallest and second-largest Pyramid, and Menkaure, the smallest Pyramid.

Sloped Angles (in degrees)	CHEOPS (Greatest)	KHAFRE (Second largest)	MENKAURE (Smallest)
Edge Angle	42 °	43.3 °	41.6 °
Slope Angle	51.84 °	53.1 °	51.3 °

Fig. 19.2
The sloped angles of the three main Pyramids of Giza.

In Fig. 19.3, the pyramid has a crossection of two **3 - 4 - 5** triangles, with the "**3**" sides as the base, and the two "**4**" sides butted up against each other. Thus the pyramid is **4** units high, and **6** (twice **3**) units across at the base.

This pyramid corresponds to the scaled down measurement of the actual measurement of the second-largest and second-tallest Pyramid Khafre.

A **3 - 4 - 5** triangle has an angle of **53.1** degrees between the **3** and **5** sides.

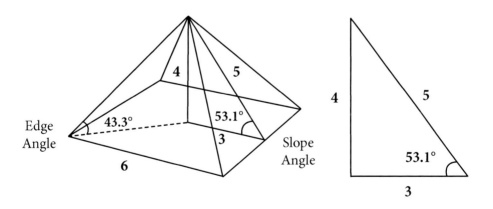

Fig. 19.3
The 3 - 4 - 5 Triangle Pyramid.

In the 17th century, Sir Isaac Newton realized that, when we separate white light using a prism (or rain drops), the visual spectrum of colored light (otherwise known as the rainbow) is produced.

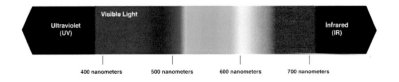

Fig. 19.4
The Visible Light Spectrum

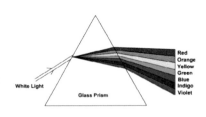

Fig. 19.5
Dispersion of the light through a Glass Prism.

Newton continued his research and wrote a New Theory of Light and Colour, in which he stated that light did not reveal colour, but was actually responsible for producing colour and reflecting it in the human eye. A typical eye can see from about **400** nm (deep purple) to about **780** nm (deep red).

Below is a table of primary and secondary rainbow angles of various wavelengths of light. with the corresponding colour and chakra.[1]

Wavelength	Primary	Secondary	Colour	Chakra
400 nm	40.5 °	53.7 °	Violet	Crown
600 nm	42.0 °	51 °	Orange	Sacral
700 nm	42.4 °	50.3 °	Red	Root

Fig. 19.6
The Primary and Secondary Rainbow, wavelength, colour and chakra.

It can be noted that while the primary angles get smaller with shorter wavelengths, the secondary angles do the opposite. The outer rainbow has its colours in reverse order to the inner one: red is on the outside of the primary bow, but is on the inside of the secondary one.

The colour sequence of a double rainbow matches the chakras of the human body (Fig. 12.2 and Fig. 12.3).

The following tables present the correlation between the three Pyramids of Giza with the information of the *Rainbow Principle* presented in Fig. 19.2 and Fig. 19.6.

Pyramid	Edge Angle	Wavelength	Colour	Chakra
CHEOPS	42 °	600 nm	Orange	Sacral
KHAFRE	43.3 °	780 nm	Deep Red	Root
MENKAURE	41.6 °	550 nm	Green	Heart

Fig. 19.7
*The correlation between the three main pyramids
of Giza and the Primary Rainbow.*

Pyramid	Slope Angle	Wavelength	Colour	Chakra
CHEOPS	51.84°	~ 562 nm	Yellow-Green	Solar Plexus Heart
KHAFRE	53.1°	~ 456 nm	Orange	Sacral
MENKAURE	51.3°	525 nm	Green	Heart

Fig. 19.8
*The correlation between the three main Pyramids of Giza
and the Secondary Rainbow.*

A face of the cube **6 x 6 x 6** or *Hypercube 216* of edge length **6** units appears naturally as the base of the Pyramid **3 - 4 - 5** in Figure 19.3.

According to the previously presented tables, the information encoded in the Pyramid **3 - 4 - 5** is intrinsically connected with the expression of light in nature. This particular Pyramid was used by the Ancient Egyptians as a prototype to build the majority of pyramids, including the Great Pyramid itself (See the Triangle **3 - 4 - 5** as shown in Fig. 1.10).
Another interesting fact, is that the coordinates of the Great Pyramid are **29.9792458° N, 31.1342880° E**. i.e.; the speed of light and the latitude numbers have exactly the same digits. The speed of light in a vacuum is **299,792,458** meters per second.
The perfect cube, *Hypercube 216,* is therefore considered to be a strong geometric foundation of light and is a bridge from the third dimension to the fourth and higher dimensions.
There is a correlation between the energy frequency voltage of the *Hypercube 216,* **2,808** and the slope angle of the Pyramid **3 - 4 - 5**, which is **53.1°**, the firmament of the secondary rainbow seen by the eye.

$$2808 = 53^2 - 1 \quad \text{and} \quad 2808 \approx 53^2 \tag{58}$$

According to Figure 5.5, in each half of the *Geometric Key* (Fig. 5.2), there are **144** purple female circles, representing a fractal element of luminic energy. According to Figure 13.8, there are **37** energy emanation points on the *third star number*. Knowing that the light has **666** possible pathways in a set of **37** energy emanation points. In terms of probability, the average number of photons flowing upward or downward per pathway is:

$$10^p \div 666 \approx 11.70 \quad \text{with} \quad p = 144 \div 37 = 3.89 \tag{59}$$

Squaring the equation (59), it leads to the equation (53), approximately equal to **137.036**, the inverse ratio of the constant *Alpha* (α), the fine structure contant. Note that the fraction p can be written using equation (58) :

$$p = 144 \div 37 = (2,808 \div 37) - 72 \tag{60}$$

2,808 ÷ **37** is the energy frequency voltage per energy point.
72 is the number of female circles in one quadrant of *the Geometric Key.*

Fig. 19.9
The Black Square by Jakub Woynarowski.

" Descent of the Cube "

"When the Gift of the Gods came in the Form of the Descent of the Cube, it not only gave us a finite boundary condition, but revealed its secret as the infinite Container of Space."

With acknowledgment: Jain 108

20. Conclusion

This book has been a condensation of my own inner convictions relating to the functions of number, shape and the energetic World around me, but I cannot at this stage reach a full conclusion, for this study is a work in progress for myself and others in this increasingly enlightened community.

In my opinion and according to my own experience in Western society, we need to rediscover again the balance between the feminine and masculine or left and right hemispheres of the brain and the World. The expression of heart energy is definitely encouraged on this path to help us better navigate our experience so we can be fulfilled from the core of our soul with the Divine wisdom that speaks through every field of study. I look forward to one day harmonizing both left and right hemispheric perspectives into a unified whole theory.

This book is concerned with the theoretical aspect of pyramid energy and the manifestation of a divine blueprint as the spiral seen everywhere in nature. Although this work has a theoretical background, the tangible energy blueprints from the numbers are available for others to expand and to accompany them on their own journey and to their own conclusions. I believe that the language of numbers is an aspect of pure consciousness that will allow us to get more solid foundations from which we are able to show our innate interconnection with The All.

Intuition is required for us to move forward, as it is a source of knowing that will assist anyone to better connect with his or her own light within. Without more widespread application of intuition and conscience as subtle guiding principles, our society deviates from its full potential in creating a peaceful and harmonious home for everyone.

The book is highly recommended to those with practical and engineering minds who can apply some 3D applications to the content. My next step is to give detail to these practical applications in order that we can improve the experience and quality of using numbers and geometry in ways that will benefit future generations. In my opinion, the deciphering of the Great Pyramid and other sacred sites in their geometric dimensions and their true function, will help us to lift the veil and understand their function more fully, as technological architecture.

This opportunity is available only if our society is ready to accept the quantum leap and be responsible for balancing feminine and masculine energy which will inevitably lead to a reintegration of this lost knowledge.

> "There will come a day when people of all races, colors, and creeds will put aside their differences. They will come together in love, joining hands in unification, to heal the Earth and all Her children. They will move over the Earth like a great Whirling Rainbow, bringing peace, understanding and healing everywhere they go. Many creatures thought to be extinct or mythical will resurface at this time; the great trees that perished will return almost overnight. All living things will flourish, drawing sustenance from the breast of our Mother, the Earth.
>
> The great spiritual Teachers who walked the Earth and taught the basics of the truths of the Whirling Rainbow Prophecy will return and walk amongst us once more, sharing their power and understanding with all. We will learn how to see and hear in a sacred manner. Men and women will be equals in the way Creator intended them to be; all children will be safe anywhere they want to go. Elders will be respected and valued for their contributions to life. Their wisdom will be sought out. The whole Human race will be called The People and there will be no more war, sickness or hunger forever."
>
> **Navajo-Hopi Prophecy of the Whirling Rainbow**

Fig. 20.1
A 2007 Rainbow Gathering in Bosnia.

A. Coordinate systems

Fig A.1
Cartesian Coordinates of a point P.

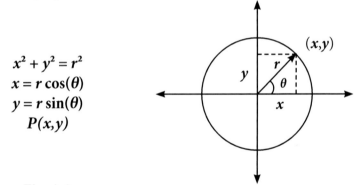

Fig. A.2
Polar Coordinates of a point P on the circle.

$$x^2 + y^2 = r^2$$
$$x = r\cos(\theta)$$
$$y = r\sin(\theta)$$
$$P(x,y)$$

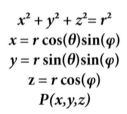

Fig. A.3
Spherical Coordinates of a point P on the sphere.

$$x^2 + y^2 + z^2 = r^2$$
$$x = r\cos(\theta)\sin(\varphi)$$
$$y = r\sin(\theta)\sin(\varphi)$$
$$z = r\cos(\varphi)$$
$$P(x,y,z)$$

B. Volume, Perimeter, Area

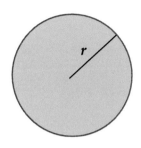

Fig. B.1
A Sphere of radius r.

Volume of the sphere : $V = (4 \div 3)\, \pi\, r^3$

Fig. B.2
A circle of radius r.

Area of the circle : $A = \pi\, r^2$

Perimeter of the circle : $P = 2\, \pi\, r$

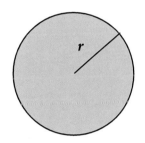

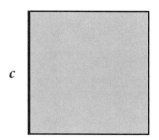

Fig. B.3
A square of edge length c.

Perimeter of the square : $4\, c$

Area of the square : c^2

Fig. B.4
A cube of edge length y.

Volume of the cube in 3D : y^3

Volume of the cube in 4D : y^4

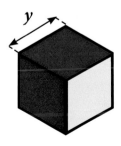

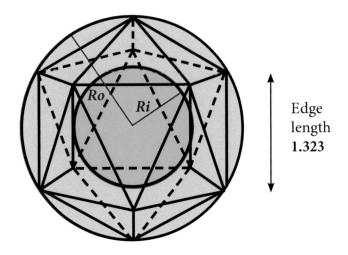

Edge length **1.323**

Fig. B.5
Icosahedron with inner and outer spheres.

The above icosahedron has an inner sphere of radius **Ri** with a value of **1** and an outer sphere of radius **Ro** with a value of **1.2584**. According to Kepler, the radius ratio of these two spheres **1.2584** was associated with the distances between Venus and Earth with an orbital ratio value of **1.3825.**

C. Squaring the circle

Squaring the circle is the challenge of constructing a square with the same area as a given circle by using only a finite number of steps with compass and straightedge. The resolution approximates the dimensions of the Great Pyramid with a base leg equal to **11** and a height equal to **7**. This gives an approximate value of *Pi* (π) equal to **22÷7** (Fig 1.10). Another approach is to take the dimensions of the Great Pyramid in relation to the *Golden Ratio Phi* (φ) **1.618**. The square of *Phi* (√φ) is the height and **2** is the base leg.

Perimeter 2 π r = 8

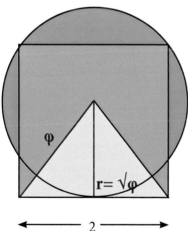

Fig. C.1
Resolution of squaring the circle.

Since the perimeter of the base of the pyramid is **8**, the Great Pyramid approximately squares the circle.

Since **4** divided by √φ is approximately equal to *Pi* (π), the circumference of a circle of radius *r* is the height of the pyramid, respecting the equation below.

$$2\,\pi\,r = 2\,\pi\sqrt{\varphi} =$$
$$2\,(4 \div \sqrt{\varphi})\,\sqrt{\varphi} = 2 \times 4 = 8$$

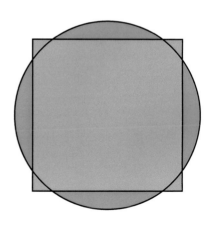

Fig. C.2
Squaring the circle.

D. The Number Pi (π)

Four different values for the number *Pi* (π) are used in this book to show the connection between the *Cornerstone 666* of the *Etheric Particle* (Fig 92), *Hypercube 216* (Fig 5.3), the Great Pyramid of Giza (Fig 8.7) and the *Golden Ratio Phi* (φ) **1.618** (Fig 1.11).

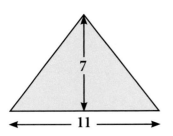

Fig. D.1
The Great Pyramid of Giza.

The number *Pi* (π) can be defined as **22÷7 = 3.142857**, the ratio between height and double the base leg.

The ratio $4 \div \sqrt{\varphi} = 3.1446055$ is calculated through the dimensions of the Great Pyramid with height $\sqrt{\varphi}$ and double base leg **4** (Fig 1.13). The resolution of squaring the circle in figures C.1 and C.2 gives this value of *Pi* (π).

The circle of diameter **666** has a perimeter *P* equal to **1,480√2**. This gives a value for *Pi* (π) equal to **3.1426968** with the formula for the perimeter defined in B.2.

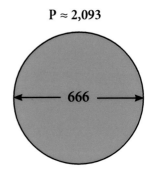

P ≈ 2,093

666

Fig. D.2
The Cornerstone 666.

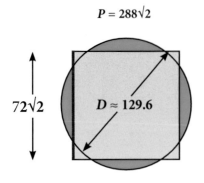

P = 288√2

72√2

D ≈ 129.6

Fig. D.3
A face of Hypercube 216.

The value of *Pi* (π) **3.14406086** is the ratio between the perimeter *P* and diameter *D* of the circle. The diameter *D* is the product of **1.27224** and edge length **72√2** of *Hypercube 216* (equation (14)).

E. The Golden Spiral

The logarithmic spiral is a spiral whose polar equation is given by

$$r(\theta) = a\,e^{b\theta} \tag{1}$$

where r is the distance from the origin, *Theta* (θ) is the angle from the x-axis, and a and b are arbitrary constants. It can be expressed parametrically as

$$x = r\cos(\theta) = a\cos(\theta)\,e^{b\theta} \tag{1a}$$
$$y = r\sin(\theta) = a\sin(\theta)\,e^{b\theta} \tag{1b}$$

The spiral is generated by Fibonacci numbers (Fig 4.1) approximating the *Golden Ratio Phi* (φ **1.618**) referred to as the *Golden Spiral*.

The polar equation for a *Golden Spiral* is the same as for other logarithmic spirals, but with a special value of the growth factor b when *Theta* (θ) is a right angle (a quarter turn in either direction). a is the initial radius of the spiral of value **1**.

Fig. E.1
The logarithmic spiral.

Equation (1) can be expressed parametrically in spherical coordinates. This leads to a new parametrisation of equation (1) expressed in the following equations (1c), (1d) and (1e).

$$X = x\sin(\varphi) = r\cos(\theta)\sin(\varphi) = a\cos(\theta)\sin(\varphi)\,e^{b\theta} \tag{1c}$$

$$Y = y\sin(\varphi) = r\sin(\theta)\sin(\varphi) = a\sin(\theta)\sin(\varphi)\,e^{b\theta} \tag{1d}$$

$$Z = r\cos(\varphi) = a\,e^{b\theta}\cos(\varphi) \tag{1e}$$

φ is the colatitude, the angle from the z-axis (Fig A.3).

F. Astronomy

The angular diameter is the angle the diameter of an object makes in the sky, also known as angular size or apparent diameter. The Moon, with an actual diameter of **2,160** miles has an angular diameter between **29'21"** (**0.489°**) and **33'30"** (**0.558°**), depending on its distance from Earth throughout the seasons.

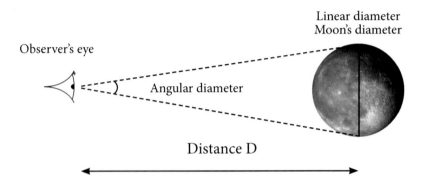

Fig. F.1
*Angular and Linear diameter for an observer's eye
from a distance D of the Moon.*

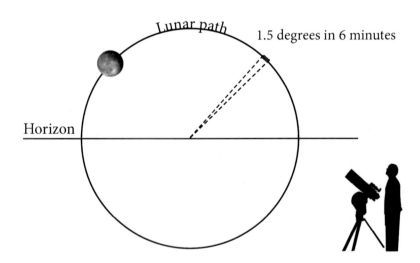

Fig. F.2
*Looking directly East the lunar path on Spring Equinox
describes a circle in a 24 hour period.*

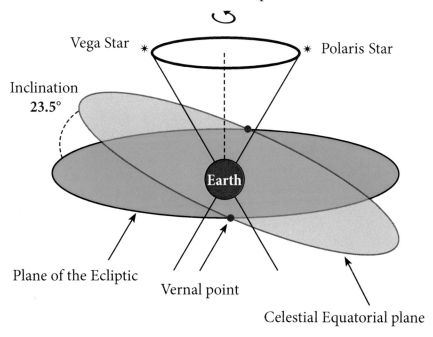

Fig. F.3
Earth's Precessional Arc of 25,920 years.

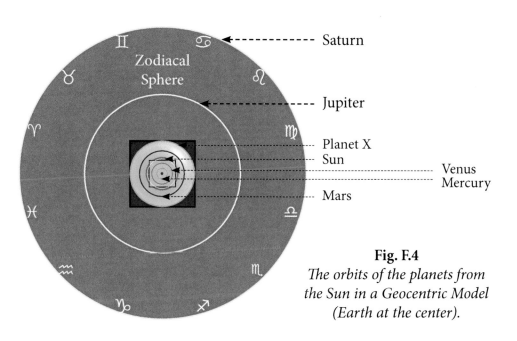

Fig. F.4
The orbits of the planets from the Sun in a Geocentric Model (Earth at the center).

G. Calendar

In Figure 15.3 the **9**th step of the Temple of Kukulkan equates to the year **2,016** and beyond. Subtracting **5,184** (a time period of **12.96** baktuns) from **2,016** brings to the year **3,168** BC. These harmonic numbers are encoded in the dimensions of the Great Pyramid since **2,016** is the height and **3,168** is the base leg. The *gematria value* for 'Lord Jesus Christ*' is **3,168**.

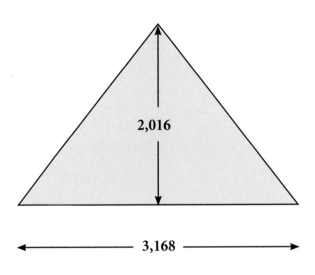

G.1
The Great Pyramid and 2,016.

The *Golden Ratio Phi* (φ) **1.618** power to **18** results in **5,778**.

$$\varphi^{18} \approx 5{,}778$$

The number **18** is the foundation stone from which the Mayan Long Count Calendar is built (Fig 14.3).

The Jewish Calendar year **5,778** equates to the year **2,018**. This value is also the temperature at the surface of the Sun in Kelvin. An exact date for the completion of the Mayan Calendar is ambiguous but appears to be anytime soon after **2,016**.

H. Constants

Astrophysical Constants

Lunar year	**364** days or **360** days
Lunar month	**29.53846154** days
(full moon to full moon)	
Solar year	**365.25** days
Light year	**5,885,374,464,000** miles
Sidereal orbital period of Venus	**224.701** days
Sidereal orbital period of Mars	**686.98** days
Sidereal orbital period of Jupiter	**4332.589** days
Sidereal orbital period of Mercury	**87.969** days

Mathematical Constants

	1.61803399
Phi (φ pronounced fye)	
phi (ϕ pronounced fee) = 1 ÷ φ	**0.61803399**
Epsilon (ε) = ϕ ÷ 2	**0.30901699**
Lambda (λ) = φ ÷ 2	**0.80901699**
Euler's constant *e*	**2.71828**
Four different values of *Pi* (π)	**3.144605; 3.1440608;**
	3.142857; 3,1426968;
Number of spiral arcs β	**14.142857**

Geophysical Constants

Earth's Radius	**3,960** miles
Meridian Circumference	**24,883.2** miles
Moon's Radius	**1,080** miles
Sun's Radius	**432, 000** miles
Earth distance from the Sun	**93,312,000** miles
Moon distance from the Earth	**233,280** miles
Venus distance from the Sun	**67,495,482** miles
Mercury distance from Earth	**35,983,198** miles
Mars distance from Earth	**141,635,701** miles
Planet X distance from Earth	**201,553,920** miles
Jupiter distance from Earth	**483,628,133** miles
Saturn distance from Earth	**887,076,068** miles
Zodiacal Sphere distance from Earth	**8,957,952,000** miles

Metrological Constants

Imperial foot	12 inches
Furlong	660 feet
Mile	5,280 feet
Reed	12.4416 feet
Egyptian Royal Cubit	20.736 inches or 1.728 feet
Egyptian digit	8.8868 inches or 0.740571 feet
Hebrew Great Cubit	24.8832 inches or 2.0736 feet
Sumerian Cubit	1.65888 feet
Megalithic Inch	0.82944 inches
Megalithic Yard	2.72 feet

Physical Constants

Speed of light	$432^2 = 186,624$ miles/sec
Energy frequency voltage of *H216*	2,808
Gravity constant	9.81 N/m^2
Fine structure constant *Alpha* (α)	$0.00729734 \approx 1/137$
Light body constant Delta (δ)	3.72241
Parameter *m* of the light body	1.65
Omega (ω)	7.783

Numerical Keys of *Hypercube 216*

Number of spins per day	*Iota* (ι) = 216/28 = 7.714
Number of spins every **9.6** hours	*Eta* (η) = 216/70 = 3.085
Square root of the edge length.	*Mu* (μ) = 6 x $2^{1/4} \approx \sqrt{51}$
Surface area of a face **10,368** divided by **3,168**.	
	Psi (Ψ) = 10,368/3,168 $\approx$ 3.28
Approximate value in meters for **1** foot.	*psi* (ψ = 1/ Ψ) $\approx$ **0.3055**
Two faces of *H216* added to the energy frequency voltage **2,808**.	
	Xi (ξ) = 1.27224

Geometrical Keys

Sacred Angle	308.571 degrees
Slope Angle of the Great Pyramid of Giza	51.84 degrees
Edge length of a single cube inside *H216*	$12\sqrt{2}$
Edge length of *H216*	$72\sqrt{2}$
Volume of a single cube inside *H216* in 4D	82,944
Volume of *H216* in 4D	107,495,424

Crop Circles

Alton Priors
East Field, Wiltshire, 3rd July 2005

Credit : Lucy Pringle.

Photographs of the four crop circles.

www.lucypringle.co.uk

Windmill Hill

Wiltshire, 19th July 1999

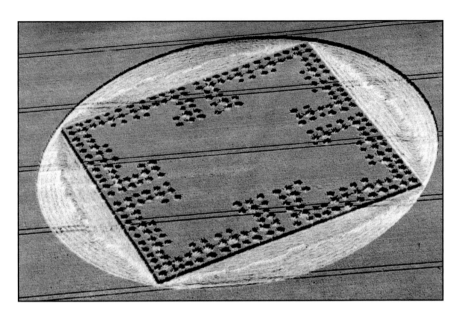

West Kennet

Wiltshire, 4th August 1999

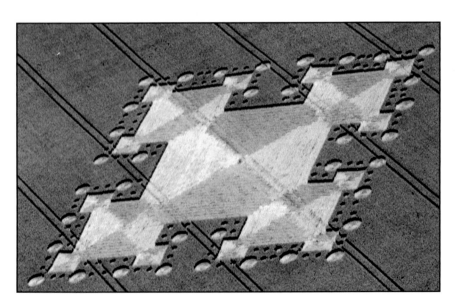

Hackpen Hill

Wiltshire, August 26th 2012

Gematria

Greek	Letter	Value	Hebrew	Letter	Value
Alpha	α	1	Aleph	א	1
Beta	β	2	Beth	ב	2
Gamma	γ	3	Gimel	ג	3
Delta	δ	4	Daleth	ד	4
Epsilon	ε	5	He	ה	5
Zeta	ζ	7	Vav	ו	6
Eta	η	8	Zayin	ז	7
Theta	θ	9	Cheth	ח	8
Iota	ι	10	Teth	ט	9
Kappa	κ	20	Yod	י	10
Lambda	λ	30	Kaph	כ,ך	20
Mu	μ	40	Lamed	ל	30
Nu	ν	50	Mem	ם מ	40
Xi	ξ	60	Nun	ן נ	50
Omicro	o	70	Camek	ס	60
Pi	π	80	Ayin	ע	70
Rho	ρ	100	Pe	ף פ	80
Sigma	σ, ς	200	Tsadey	ץ צ	90
Tau	τ	300	Qoph	ק	100
Upsilon	υ	400	Resh	ר	200
Phi	φ	500	Shin	ש	300
Chi	χ	600	Tav	ת	400
Psi	ψ	700			
Omega	ω	800			

All things	παντα	432
All Nations	כלגוים	432
Amethyst	αμεθυστος	1,225
Andrew	Ανδρεας	361
Asher	Ασηρ	309
Benjamin	Βενιαμιν	168
Beryl	βηρυλλος	840
Bethlehem	Βηθλεεμ	432
Chalcedony	Χαλκηδων	1,513
Child	ילד	44
Christ	χριστος	1,480
Chrysolyte	Χρυσολιθος	1,689
Chrysophrasus	Χρυσοπρασος	2,021
City of my God	της πολεως Θεου μου	3,456
Emerald	σμαραγδος	619
Father	אב	3
Foundation	יסד	74
Gad	Γαδ	8
Gethsemane	Γεθσημανι	432

In the beginning God created the heaven and the earth

את השמים ואת הארץ ברא בראשית אהים 2,701

Issachar	Ισσαχαρ	1,112
Jacinth	υακινθινος	820
James	Ιακωβος	1,103
James (Son of Alpheus)	Ιακωβος Αλφαιου	2,115
Jasper	ιασπις	501
Jerusalem	ירושלם	432
Jesus	ιησους	888
Jesus-Christ	ιησους χριστος	2,368
John	Ιωαννης	1,119
Joseph	Ιωσηφ	1,518
Judah	Ιουδα	485
Judas	Ιουδας	685
Kabbalah	קבלה	137
Levi	Λευι	445
Light	המאור	252

Lebbaeus	Λεββαιος	320
Levi (Matthew)	Λευι	445
Lord Jesus-Christ	*Κυριος ιησους χριστος*	3,168
Love	אהב	8
Manasses	Μανασσης	700
Mother	אמ	41
Nathanael	Ναθαναηλ	150
Nepthalim	Νεφθαλειμ	650
Peter	πετρος	755
Pharez (The Breaker)	רפץ	370
Philip	Φιλιππος	980
Reuben	Ρουβην	630
Sapphire	σαπφειρος	1,166
Sardius	σαρδιον	435
Sardonyx	σαρδονυξ	885
Scarlet Thread	חוט השני	388
Scarlet	שני	360
Sheen Nun Yod	ישן	360
Simeon	Συμεων	1,495
Simon	Σιμων ο καναναιος	1,573
Son of Man	μιο στουανθρ ωπου	2,960
Thomas	Θωμας	1,050
Topaz	τοπαζος	728
Two Great Lights	המאודת הגדלים	744
Victory	נצח	148
Water from the rock	רמים ממסלע	296
Whole	שלם and ολος	370
Zebulon	Ζαβουλων	1,360

The Temple of Solomon

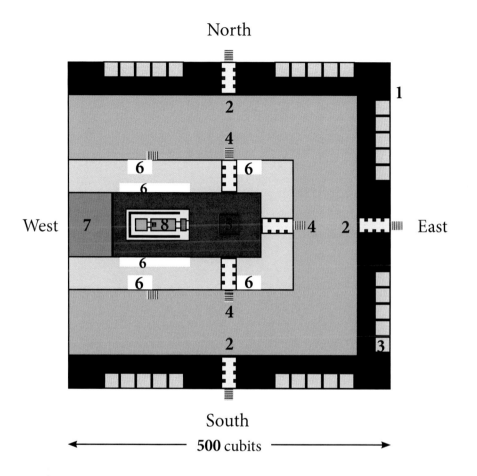

North

1

West   7   8   4   2   East

South

500 cubits

1. "He measured the area on all four sides. It had a wall around it, five hundred cubits long and five hundred cubits wide, to separate the holy from the common. *Ezekiel 42:20*
2. Three gates in the outer wall and six little guard-chambers within each gate. *Ezekiel 40:6,20,24.*
3. Chambers.
4. Three gates from the outer courtyard to the inner courtyard
5. The Altar. *Ezekiel 43:13-17*
6. The Priests' chambers
7. The western building.
8. The Holy Temple.

Inside the Holy Temple

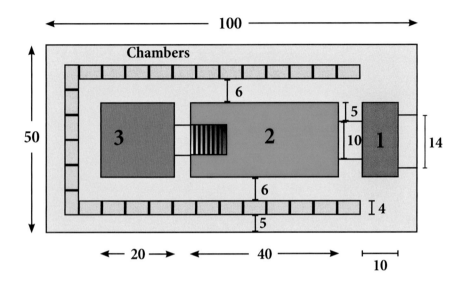

The ground plans of the Temple and Holy Temple of Solomon come from the Koren Jerusalem Bible. The measurements of the Holy Temple come from Chapter 1, King 6.

1. The Porch, **23** cubits height, **10** cubits long and **20** cubits wide.
2. The Temple, **30** cubits height, **40** cubits long and **20** cubits wide.
3. The Sanctuary, **20** cubits height, long and wide.

On the next page is the ground floor of the Temple of Solomon showing only the Holy Temple and the Altar in colours. The inside and outside courtyard, the gates and the thirty chambers along the pavement are depicted with a red line. Figure 2.18 is the combination of this ground floor rotated three times **90** degrees clockwise.

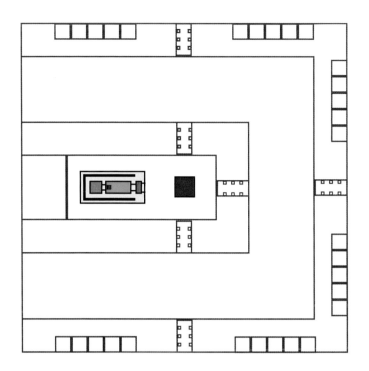

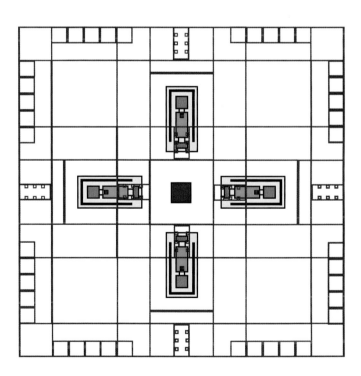

Glossary

Axiom : a statement or preposition on which an abstractly defined structure is based.

Altar : a table or flat-topped block used as the focus for a religious ritual.

Alchemy : a process of transformation, creation, or combination.

Amethyst : a precious stone consisting of a violet or purple variety of quartz.

Anti-clockwise : in the opposite direction to the way in which the hands of a clock move around.

Anti-gravity : the antithesis of gravity; a hypothetical force by which a body of positive mass would repel a body of
negative mass.

Ark of Covenant : the wooden chest which contained the tablets of the laws of the ancient Israelites.

Atlantis : a legendary island, first mentioned by Plato, said to have existed in the Atlantic Ocean west of Gibraltar and to have sunk beneath the sea.

Atom : the smallest particle of a chemical element, consisting of a positively charged nucleus (containing protons and typically also neutrons) surrounded by negatively charged electrons.

Avebury : The largest ceremonial megalithic structures in Europe.

Baktun : 20 katun cycles of the ancient Maya Long Count Calendar containing 144,000 days.

Beryl : transparent pale green, blue or yellow mineral consisting of a silicate of beryllium and aluminium, sometimes used as a gemstone.

Bethlehem : Palestinian city located in the central West Bank, Palestine, about 6.2 miles south of Jerusalem.

Blueprint : something which acts as a plan, model, or template.

Binary : using a system of numerical notation with two as its base, employing the digits 0 and 1.

Capstone : a finishing stone of a structure.

Centre of mass : a point representing the mean position of the matter in a body or system.

Centrifugal : moving away from a centre.

Centripetal : moving toward a centre.

Chakra : each of seven centres of spiritual power in the human body.

Christ Circle : a circle of perimeter 1,480, gematria value of Christ, hence the name 'Christ Circle'.

Christ Sphere : a Sphere of radius 235.45 feet, the edge of the outside wall of the New Jerusalem.

Chalcedony : quartz occurring in a micro-crystalline form such as onyx and agate.

Chi : the circulating life force whose existence and properties are the basis of much Chinese philosophy and medicine.

Chrysolite : a yellowish-green or brownish variety of olivine, used as a gemstone.

Chrysoprase : an apple-green gemstone consisting of a variety of chalcedony that contains nickel.

Circumference : the outer boundary, especially of a circular area; perimeter.

Clockwise : in a curve corresponding in direction to the movement of the hands of a clock.

Convex : having an outline or surface curved like the exterior of a circle or sphere.

Concave : having an outline or surface that curves inwards like the interior of a circle or sphere.

Concentric : having a common center, as circles or spheres.

Consciousness : the state of being conscious and responsive to one's surroundings.

Convoluted : intricately folded, twisted, or coiled.

Correlation : a mutual relationship of interdependence between two or more things.

Cornerstone : A stone at the corner of a building uniting two intersecting walls.

Cosine : the sine of the complement of a given angle or arc.

Cosmology : the science of the origin and development of the universe.

Cosmogony : the branch of science concerned with the origin of the universe, especially the solar system.

Cube : symmetrical three-dimensional shape contained by six equal squares.

Cubit : an ancient linear unit based on the length of the fore arm, from elbow to the tip of the middle finger, usually from 17 to 21 inches (43 to 53cm).

Crop circle : an area of standing crops which has been flattened in the form of a circle or more complex pattern by an unexplained agency.

Crystallized water : Frozen water crystallized into beautiful geometric patterns.

Crystal skull : The crystal skulls are human skull hard stone carvings made of clear or milky white quartz.

Cymatics : The study of sound and vibration made visible, typically on the surface of a plate, diaphragm or membrane.

Decagon : a polygon having ten angles and ten sides.

Digit : the breadth of a finger used as a unit of linear measure, usually equal to 3/4 inch (2 cm).

Dodecagon : plane figure with twelve straight sides and angles.

Dodecahedron : three-dimensional shape having twelve plane faces, in particular a regular solid figure with twelve pentagonal faces.

Double star tetrahedron : two interlocking tetrahedrons.

Double rainbow : a phenomenon in which two rainbows appear.

Eccentric : not placed centrally or not having its axis or other part placed centrally.

Electromagnetism : relating to the interrelation of electric currents or fields and magnetic fields.

Electron : a stable negatively charged subatomic particle with a mass 1,836 less than that of the proton, found in all atoms and acting as the primary carrier of electricity in solids.

Emerald : a bright green precious stone consisting of a chromium-rich variety of beryl.

Enneagram : Geometric pattern of the divine energetic flow traced inside a nonagon and creating a third field.

Entropy : a thermodynamic quantity representing the unavailability of a system's thermal energy for conversion into mechanical work, often interpreted as the degree of disorder or randomness in the system.

Energy frequency voltage : a force or potential difference expressed in units of energy, frequency or volts.

Equinox : The time or date (twice each year, about 22 September and 20 March) at which the sun crosses the celestial equator, when day and night are of equal length.

Equivalent mass : the mass of substance that displaces an entity from another molecule to create a unit valency.

Ether : a substance formerly postulated to permeate all space and to transmit light.

Etheric Particle : a particle unifying Spirit with the four interactive forces, Electromagnetism, Gravity, Strong and Weak nuclear. A universal geometric template encoded in the architecture of many ancient temples.

Fibonacci spiral : an approximation of the golden spiral created by drawing circular arcs connecting the opposite corners of squares in the Fibonacci tiling; this one uses squares of sizes 1, 1, 2, 3, 5, 8, 13, 21, and 34.

Fibonacci flower : the seed pattern of a sunflower formed by a spinning Fibonacci spiral.

Fine structure constant : fundamental physical constant characterizing the strength of the electromagnetic interaction between elementary charged particles.

Finger breadth : the breadth of a finger: approximately 3/4 inch (2 cm).

Firmament : the vault of heaven; sky.

Flower of life : a geometric pattern consisting of overlapping circles.

Fractal : a curve or geometrical figure, each part of which has the same statistical character as the whole.

Fractal 44 : a fractal pattern of 44 squares from the Alton Priors crop circle formation.

Genome : a full set of chromosomes; all the inheritable traits of an organism.

Gematria : Kabbalistic method of interpreting the Hebrew scriptures by computing the numerical value of words, based on the values of their constituent letters.

Geocentric model : having or representing the earth as the centre, as in former astronomical systems.

Geodesic : relating to or denoting the shortest possible line between two points on a sphere or other curved surface.

Geomancy : the art of arranging buildings auspiciously.

Geometry : 'Geo-metry', from the Greek 'Geo' meaning 'Earth' and 'Metron' meaning 'To measure' which together literally translate as the 'Measuring of the earth' or 'Earthly measurements'.

Geometric Key : the geometric key is the geometric combination of three crop circles, Alton Priors (3rd July *2005)*, Windmill Hill (19th July 1999) and West Kennet (4th August *1999)*.

Gethsemane : Garden at the foot of the Mount of Olives in Jerusalem.

Glastonbury Abbey : a monastery in Glastonbury, Somerset, England.

Gnomon : the projecting piece on a sundial that shows the time by its shadow.

Golden ratio : a special number Phi φ found by dividing a line into two parts so that the longer part divided by the smaller part is equal to the whole length divided by the longer part.

Golden spiral : a logarithmic spiral whose growth factor is Phi (φ), the golden ratio. That is, a golden spiral gets wider by a factor Phi (φ) for every quarter turn it makes.

Gravity : the force that attracts a body towards the centre of the earth, or towards any other physical body having mass.

Helical : having the shape or form of a helix; spiral.

Heliocentric model : having or representing the sun as the centre, as in the accepted astronomical model of the solar system.

Helix : an object having a three-dimensional shape like that of a wire wound uniformly in a single layer around a cylinder cone, as in a corkscrew or spiral staircase.

Hendecagon : plane figure with eleven straight sides and angles.

Heptagram : a seven-pointed star formed by drawing a continuous line in seven straight segments.

Hexagon : a polygon having six angles and six sides.

Holy Temple of Solomon : the Holy Temple is constituted of the Porch, the Temple and the Sanctuary in the centre of the inner courtyard.

Homogeneous : consisting of parts all of the same kind.

Horocycle : a curve whose normal or perpendicular geodesics all converge closely in the same direction.

Horus : A god of ancient Egypt in the form of a falcon whose right eye was the sun or morning star, representing power and quintessence, and whose left eye was the moon or evening star, representing healing.

Hyperbolic geometry : geometry taking curvature into consideration.

Hypercube : a geometrical figure in four or more dimensions which is analogous to a cube in three dimensions.

Hypercube 216 : A 6 x 6 x 6 cube consisting of 216 single cubes having the uniqueness of respecting the equation found by the American Philosopher D. G. Leahy.

Icosagon : a twenty-sided polygon.

Icosahedron : a three-dimensional shape having twenty plane faces, in particular a regular solid figure with twenty equal triangular faces.

Implosion : collapse violently inwards.

Interior angle : an angle formed within a polygon by two adjacent sides.

Interval : the difference in pitch between two sounds.

Isis : Goddess of ancient Egypt.

Isotropic : having the same magnitude or properties when measured in different directions.

Jacinth : a reddish-orange gem variety of zircon.

Jasper : an opaque reddish-brown variety of chalcedony.

Jerusalem : Ancient holy city in the Judean Mountains.

Kabbalah : an esoteric method, discipline, and school of thought that originated in Judaism.

Lemuria : a hypothetical "lost land" variously located in the Indian and Pacific Oceans.

Levitation : rise or cause to rise and hover in the air.

Levite : a member of the Hebrew tribe of Levi, in particular an assistant to the priests in the Jewish temple.

Light body : etheric, auric or intangible energy field surrounding the body.

Light code : numerical keys of the ether involving counts of six or seven applied through the number 111.

Light year : a unit of distance equivalent to the distance that light travels in one year, 9.4607×10^{12} km (nearly 6 million million miles).

Luminic : relating to light.

Macrocosm : the whole of a complex structure, especially the world or the universe, contrasted with a small or representative part of it.

Magnetic field : a region around a magnetic material or a moving electric charge within which the force of magnetism acts.

Mainstream science : mainstream science is scientific inquiry in an established field of study that does not depart significantly from orthodox theories.

Mandala : Sanskrit term that means 'circle' or 'discoid object'.

Megalithic yard : a unit of measurement of about 2.72 feet (0.83 m) that some researchers believe was used in the construction of megalithic structures.

Menstrual cycle : the process of ovulation and menstruation in women and other female primates.

Metrology : scientific study of measurement.

Microcosm : a thing regarded as encapsulating in miniature the characteristics of something much larger.

Mu : a suggested lost continent located in the Pacific Ocean between Asia and America.

Music of the spheres : an ancient philosophical concept that regards proportions in the movements of celestial bodies — the Sun, Moon, and planets — as a form of music.

Newgrange : the largest of three mound covered passage graves on the river Boyne in county Meath, Ireland, built in 3000 BC.

New Jerusalem : Ezekiel's prophetic vision of a city centred on the rebuilt Holy Temple, the Third Temple, to be established in Jerusalem, which would be the capital of the Messianic Kingdom, the meeting place of the twelve tribes of Israel, during the Messianic era; also heaven regarded as the prototype of the earthly Jerusalem; the heavenly city.

Node : points of no displacement - remain in the same position. The ether vibrates with zero displacement.

Nuclear force : the strong attractive force that holds nucleons together in the atomic nucleus.

Number of the Beast : a term in the Book of Revelation, of the New Testament, that is associated with the Beast of Revelation in chapter 13.

Numerical key : fundamental numbers.

Octagon : a plane figure with eight straight sides and eight angles.

Octahedron : a tree-dimensional shape having eight planes faces, in particular a regular solid figure with eight equal triangular faces.

Onyx : a semi-precious variety of agate with different colours in layers.

Orbital motion : motion of an object in an orbit around a fixed point; planets, electrons, satellites in orbital rotation.

Orbital period : period of the orbit of an object; planets, electrons, satellites in orbital rotation.

Osiris : the Egyptian god killed and disserted by his brother, Set, and reconstructed by his wife, Isis, and their avenging son, Horus.

Palm : a linear measure of from 3 to 4 inches (7.5 to 10cm), based on the breadth of the finger.

Particle Physics : the branch of physics concerned with the properties, relationships, and interactions of subatomic particles.

Pentagram : a five-pointed star formed by drawing a continuous line in five straight segments.

Perfect fourth : an interval spanning four consecutive notes in a diatonic scale.

Perfect fifth : an interval spanning five consecutive notes in a diatonic scale.

Perimeter : the border or outer boundary of a two-dimensional figure.

Petrosphere : any roughly spherical artefact made of stone.

Photon : a quantum of electromagnetic radiation, usually considered as an elementary particle that is its own antiparticle and that has zero rest mass and char and a spin of one.

Photon flux : the number of photons per second per unit area.

Planetary system : a set gravitationally bound non-stellar objects in orbit around a star or star system.

Platonic solids : a regular, convex polyhedron. The five regular solids, tetrahedron, cube, octahedron, dodecahedron and icosahedron.

Polarity : the property of having poles or being polar.

Poles : each of the two opposite points of a magnet at which magnetic forces are strongest.

Polyhedron : a solid figure with many plane faces, typically more than six.

Polygon : a figure, especially a closed plane figure, having three or more, usually straight, sides.

Prana : breath, considered as a life-giving force.

Precession of the equinoxes : motion of the equinoxes along the ecliptic (the plane of Earth's orbit) caused by the cyclic precession of Earth's axis of rotation.

Pyramid energy : energy generated inside a Pyramid.

Quantification : express or measure the quantity of.

Quantum theory : a theory of matter and energy based on the concept of quanta.

Quartz : a hard mineral consisting of silica, typically occurring as colourless or white hexagonal prisms.

Rainbow Principle : Rainbows are formed when light from the sun is scattered by water droplets (e.g. raindrops or fog) through a process called refraction. Refraction occurs when the light from the sun changes direction when passing through a medium denser than air, such as a raindrop. Once the refracted light enters the raindrop, it is reflected off the back and then refracted again as it exits and travels to our eyes.

Reed : an ancient unit of length, equal to 6 cubits.

Regular polygon : a polygon that is equiangular (all angles are equal in measure) and equilateral (all sides have the same length).

Rhombus : a quadrilateral whose sides all have the same length.

Rhombic dodecahedron : a convex polyhedron with 12 congruent rhombic faces.

Rosslyn Chapel : a chapel sitting six miles south of Edinburgh, Scotland's ancient capital city.

Sacred Angle : angle extracted from a seven-pointed star.

Sacred Geometry : geometry involving sacred universal patterns used in the designs of everything in our reality, most often seen in sacred architecture and sacred art. Geometry and mathematical ratios, harmonics and proportions are also found in music, light, cosmology, ether.

Sapphire : a transparent precious stone, typically blue, which is a form of corundum.

Sardius : red precious stone mentioned in the Bible (Exodus 28:17) and in classical writings, probably ruby or carnelian.

Sardonyx : onyx in which white layers alternate with sard (solid-colored chalcedony quartz).

Sarsen circle : main circle composed of 30 upright stones in Stonehenge.

Schumann Resonance : the resonant frequency of the Earth's atmosphere, between the surface and the densest part of the ionosphere.

Seed of life pattern : seven interlocking circles.

Silicate : any of the largest group of mineral compounds, as quartz, beryl, garnet, feldspar, mica, and various kinds of clay.

Sine : a mathematical function of a given angle or arc.

Solstice : either of the two occasions in the year when the sun is directly above either the furthest point north or the furthest point south of the equator that it ever reaches. These are the times in the year, in the middle of the summer or winter, when there are the longest hours of day or night.

Space-time : the concepts of time and three-dimensional space regarded as fused in a four dimensional continuum.

Span : The distance from the tip of the thumb to the tip of the little finger when the hand is fully extended, formerly used as a unit of measure equal to about 9 inches (23 centimeters).

Spin : turn or cause to turn round quickly.

Squaring the circle : the insoluble problem of constructing, by the methods of Euclidean geometry, a square equal in area to a given circle.

Standard model : a theory of fundamental interactions in which the electromagnetic, weak, and strong interactions are described in terms of the exchange of virtual particles.

Standing wave interferences : a standing wave pattern is a vibrational pattern produced as the result of the repeated interference of two waves of identical frequency while moving in opposite directions along the same medium.

Stanton Drew : A village near Bristol most famous for its prehistoric Stanton Drew stone circles, the largest being the Great Circle, a henge monument consisting of the second largest stone circle in Britain.

Star number : A star number is a centered figurate number, a centered hexagram, such as the Star of David, or the board Chinese checkers is played on. The nth star number is given by the formula $S^n = 6n(n − 1) + 1$. The first 4 star numbers are 1, 13, 37 and 73.

Step pyramid : a step pyramid is an architectural structure that uses flat platforms, or steps, receding from the ground up, to achieve a completed shape similar to a geometric pyramid.

Stone sphere : an assortment of over three hundred petrospheres in Costa Rica, located on the Diquís Delta and on Isla del Caño.

Stonehenge : Prehistoric monument   the English county of Wiltshire; Neolithic henge monument.

Subatomic : smaller than or occurring within an atom.

Sunspot : Sunspots are temporary phenomena on the photosphere of the Sun that appear as dark spots compared with surrounding regions.

Tabernacle : a tent used as a sanctuary for the Ark of Covenant by the Israelites during the Exodus.

Tesseract : the generalization of a cube to four dimensions.

Tetractys : a triangular figure consisting of ten points arranged in four rows: one, two, three and four points in each row, which is the geometrical representation of the fourth triangular number.

Tetrahedron : a solid having four plane triangular faces.

Thermic : relating to heat.

Thermodynamics : the branch of science concerned with the relations between heat and other forms of energy involved in physical and chemical processes.

Tiahuanaco : megalithic masonry carved with geometric and animal designs, stone statues, polychrome pottery and bronze artefacts based in Peru and Bolivia.

Topaz : a precious stone, typically colourless yellow, or pale blue, consisting of a fluorine containing aluminium silicate.

Toroidal energetic field : energy field having the shape of a torus.

Torsion : the condition of being twisted or turned.

Torus : a surface or solid resembling a ring doughnut, formed by rotating a closed curve about a line which lies in the same plane but does not intersect it.

Transmutation : change into another nature, substance, form or condition.

Transportation : the act or process of moving energy from one place to another.

Tree of life : a mystical and magical tree well known throughout many cultures, dating back to ancient times.

Triangular number : the triangular number is a figurative number that can be represented in the form of a triangular grid of points where the first row contains a single element and each subsequent row contains one more element than the previous one.

Trigonometric function : a function of an angle, as sine or cosine, expressed as the ratio of the sides of a right triangle.

Trigonometry : the branch of mathematics concerned with the relations of the sides and angles of triangles and with the relevant functions of any angles.

Tritone : an interval of three whole tones (an augmented fourth), as between C and F sharp.

Vacuum : a space entirely devoid of matter.

Valency : a measurement that shows the number of hydrogen atoms that can combine with one atom of a particular chemical element to make a compound, used to describe how easily an element can connect in a chemical way with others.

Vesica Piscis : a shape that is the intersection of two disks with the same radius, intersecting in such a way that the center of each disk lies on the perimeter of the other.

Vibration : an oscillation of the parts of a fluid or an elastic solid whose equilibrium has been disturbed or of an electromagnetic wave.

Vernal point : the point on the celestial sphere where the path of the sun crosses the celestial equator at the vernal equinox.

Vertex : a meeting point of two lines that form an angle.

Vortex : a region in a fluid in which the flow rotates around an axis line, which may be straight or curved.

Wave : a wave is an oscillation accompanied by a transfer of energy that travels through a medium (space or mass).

Wavelength : distance between corresponding points of two consecutive waves.

Yang : the active male principle of the universe, characterised as male and creative and associated with heaven, heat, and light. Contrasted with Yin.

Yin : the passive female principle of the universe, characterized as female and sustaining and associated with earth, dark and cold. Contrasted with Yang.

Yin-Yang symbol : a circle divided by an S-shaped line into a dark and a light segment, representing respectively yin and yang, each containing a 'seed' of the other.

Zero Energy Point : a gateway of space-time producing the Golden Spiral from the Divine Source emanating from the Zero in the number 101.

Zodiacal sign : one of the twelve constellations along the path of the ecliptic.

Zodiac : an imaginary belt of the heavens, extending about 8° on each side of the ecliptic, within which are the apparent paths of the sun, moon, and principal planets. It contains twelve constellations and hence twelve divisions called signs of the zodiac.

Source of the Pictures

The four creatures, Christian symbols on the front cover are from Louisa Twining's 'Symbols and Emblems of Early and Mediaeval Christian Art'.

Fig. 1. 6 Djoser's Step Pyramid, photo by Raji Sunderkrishnan.

Fig. 1. 7 Temple of Kukulkan, photo by Nikita Shvetsov.

Fig. 1.17 Great Pyramid of Egypt, photo by Simon Berger.

Fig. 2.2 Alton Priors crop circle, photo by Lucy Pringle.
www.lucypringle.co.uk

Fig. 2.6 Symbol of Mu from William Niven's stone Tablet 1231.
Discoveries in the Valley of Mexico.

Fig. 2.12 Windmill Hill crop circle, photo by Lucy Pringle.

Fig. 2.13 West Kennet crop circle, photo by Lucy Pringle.

Fig. 2.17 Ground plan of the Temple of Solomon from Koren Jerusalem.

Fig. 3.1 Vortex water, photo by Ben Ponsford, Flickr.
Aloe polyphylla, photo by Rosemary Stewart, Flickr.
Snail's shell, photo by Glen K. Peterson, Flickr.

Fig. 3.2 Cross section of an apple, photo by JB Wolfer, Flickr.

Fig. 3.6 Sunflower seed, photo by Jinky Dabon, Flickr.

Fig. 3.7 National Museum of Mathematics momath.org

Fig. 4.1 Design by Romain on Wikipedia - Fibonacci Spiral over tiled squares.

Fig. 5.1 Hackpen Hill crop circle, photo by Lucy Pringle.

Fig. 5.8 Vaulting and Cubes in Rosslyn Chapel, photo by Johan Dreue.
Author of the book "La révélation du 3ème Temple".

Fig. 6.1 Entrance of Newgrange, photo by Art Lewry, Flickr.

Fig. 6.2 Snail's shell, photo by Glen K. Peterson, Flickr.

Fig. 6.3 Image by ancient-wisdom. Petrosphere, found at Towie, Aberdeenshire.

Fig. 6.4 Cymatic patterns from Hans Jenny.

Fig. 6.5 Cymatics: A Study of Wave Phenomena.

Fig. 7.6 Section of an apple, Martha Ann, Flickr.
Starfish, Charlene, Flickr.
Starfruit, Nicholas Noyes, Flickr.
Flower, Dinesh Valke, Flickr.

Fig. 8.10 Stonehenge, photo by Pierre Jaquet, Flickr.

Fig. 9.1, 16.2, 16.3 and painting illustrated in acknowledgments.
Painted by Hannamari Mäkelä. www.hannamarimakela.com

Fig. 10.11 Rosslyn Chapel 1835. Rosslyn Chapel, Roslin, Midlothian

Fig. 11.2 Egyptian cubit rod, photo by Schwab-Schlott, Adelheid.

Fig. 11.7 Sundial, photo by Michael Tyack.

Fig. 11.8 Stanton Drew, photo by the author.

Fig. 12.1 Embryonic cell division, picture by Space Navy Magazine.

Fig. 12.10 Osiris in the Temple of Abydos, photo by Sebastian Morel, Prezi.

Fig. 13.7 Prasat Thom Koh Ker Step, photo by Guillén Pérez, Flickr.
Djoser's Step Pyramid, photo by Raji Sunderkrishnan.
Temple of Kukulkan, photo by Rob Wildwood.

Fig. 14.7 Great Sphinx of Egypt, photo by Raji Sunderkrishnan.

Fig. 14.8 Tibetan Crystal Skull Amar.
Providers of high quality energized crystal skulls.
http://www.crystalskulls.com

Fig. 14.10 Einstein the crystal skull, photo by Carolyn.
einsteinthecrystalskull.com

Fig. 14.11 Bob the crystal skull, photo by Cece Stevens.

Fig. 15.4 Photo by Zdeněk Macháček

Fig. 15.5-15.8 Diagrams from J. Giesen,
http://www.geoastro.de/geocentric/

Fig. 16.7 Photo by the author Salah-Eddin Gherbi.
Stone belonging to Tanya Greenangel.

Fig. 16.8 Newgrange's entrance, photo by Rob Geraghty, Flickr.

Fig. 16.9 Water vortex.
Feature design - William Pye.
Engineering design - Devin Consulting Ltd.

Fig. 16.10 Sungate, photo by Jeppe Lyngso.
Stone of Costa Rica, photo by Anita Gould, Flickr.
Large stone at Balbeek, photo by David Holt, Flickr.

Fig. 17.1 A colored-in version of the famed 1888 Flammarion. Design by Raven.

Fig. 17.4 The matryoshka, photo by the author Salah-Eddin Gherbi.
Painting of Mount Meru. Photo by Carmen Mensink
http://www.mandala-painting.com/

Fig. 17.5 Nun, the primeval waters lifting the boat.
Artwork from the Book of the Dead of Anhai, 1,050 BC.

Fig. 17.6 Cosmas Indicopleustes' diagram.
From Flammarion's Astronomical Myths, 1877.

Fig. 17.12 New Jerusalem Gemstones of Revelation 21:18-20.
From Christian Evidence.

Fig. 17.14 The Ark of Covenant, photo by Michael Tyack.
Ark belonging to Hugh Le Prevost.

Fig. 17.15 The Coffer in the King's chamber, photo by Howard
Middleton-jones (Desertman Photography).

Fig. 19.9 The Black Square, p 167, by Jakub Woynarowski, from the cycle
Wunderkamera, photo: courtesy of the artist.
https://culture.pl/en/artist/jakub-woynarowski

Fig. 20.1 A 2007 Rainbow Gathering in Bosnia, p 168, picture by Mladifilozof.
https://en.wikipedia.org/wiki/Rainbow_Family

Some vector graphics added throughout the book are from freesvg.org

References

Chapter 1

[1] Plato, *Gorgias*, 508, translation by J. Harward, GBWW, vol.7, p 284.

[2] Bonnie Gaunt, *The Stones and the Scarlet Thread*, p 51.

[3] John Michell with Allan Brown, *How the World Is Made, The Story of Creation According to Sacred Geometry*, Inner Traditions, 2009, pp. 40 and 42.

Chapter 2

[1] Aristotle, Metaphysica, 3-1078b.

Chapter 3

[1] Ludwig Wittgenstein. Tractatus Logico Philosophicus, New York, 1922.

[2] Ashish Dalela, Quantum Meaning: A Semantic Interpretation of Quantum Theory.

[3] Carl H. Claudy, Foreign Countries (1925).

Chapter 4

[1] Miranda Lundy in Sacred Geometry (2001).

[2] Bonnie Gaunt, *The Stones and the Scarlet Thread*, p 30.

Chapter 5

[1] D.G. Leahy, *Foundation: Matter the Body Itself* (Albany, 1996), Section III.5, pp. 433ff.

[2] Einstein, Albert. What I believe.

Chapter 6

[1] The architect Paul Jacques Grillo, Form Function and Design (1960).

Chapter 7

[1] Bonnie Gaunt, *The Stones and the Scarlet Thread*, p 33.

Chapter 8

[1] Bonnie Gaunt, *The Stones and the Scarlet Thread*, p 9.
[2] Ibid, p 196.

Chapter 9

[1] Bligh Bond, The Gate of Remembrance (Blackwell) Figure 13.
[2] Bonnie Gaunt, *The Stones and the Scarlet Thread*, p 177.
[3] Ibid, p 152.

Chapter 10

[1] Bonnie Gaunt, *The Stones and the Scarlet Thread*, p 36.
[2] Ibid, p 61.
[3] Ibid, p 23.
[4] Ibid, p 9.
[5] Ibid, p 210.
[6] Ibid, p 180.
[7] Ibid, p 81.

Chapter 11

[1] John Michell, *The Temple at Jerusalem : a Revelation*, p 47.
[2] Ibid.
[3] William L. Hosch, *The Britannica Guide to Numbers and Measurement*.
[4] John Michell, *The Temple at Jerusalem : a Revelation*, p 50.
[5] Translation by Paul Shorey, *Plato : The Collected Dialogues*, Eds. Edith Hamilton & Huntington Cairns, Princeton University Press, Princeton, N. J., 1961, (p.775)
[6] Bonnie Gaunt, *The Stones and the Scarlet Thread*, p 26.

Chapter 12

[1] Carl Jung in Mysterium Coniunctionis.
[2] Bonnie Gaunt, *The Stones and the Scarlet Thread*, p 36.
[3] Ibid, p 28.
[4] Ibid, p 170.
[5] Bligh Bond & Lea, *Gematria A Preliminary Investigation of the Cabala*, chapter 'Cephas the name given

by our Lord to Peter'.
Chapter 14

[1] W.J Wilkins, *Hindu Mythology : Vedic and Puranic*, Heritage Publishers, New Delhi, 1991, p.353.

[2] Chris Morton and Ceri Louise Thomas, T*he Mystery of the Crystal Skull, unlocking the secrets of the Past, Present and Future*, p 283.

[3] Ian Xel Lungold from his Lecture, Oct 9th, 2004, Calgary Alberta.

Chapter 16

[1] Richard Feynman, Richard P. Feynman (1985). *QED: The Strange Theory of Light and Matter*. Princeton University Press. p. 129. ISBN 0-691-08388-6.

[2] Max Born, Arthur I. Miller (2009), *Deciphering the Cosmic Number: The Strange Friendship of Wolfgang Pauli and Carl Jung*, W.W. Norton & Co., p. 253.

[3] Bonnie Gaunt, *The Stones and the Scarlet Thread*, p 86.

Chapter 17

[1] British Museum MSS ADD 18366.

[2] Stirling, *The Canon*, p 34.

[3] Marke Pawson, *Gematria, the Numbers of Infinity*, p 10.

[4] Bonnie Gaunt, *The Stones and the Scarlet Thread*, p 91.

[5] Ibid, p 169.

[6] Marke Pawson, *Gematria, the Numbers of Infinity*, p 11.

[7] Bonnie Gaunt, *The Stones and the Scarlet Thread*, p 87.

[8] Ibid, p 52-53.

Chapter 19

[1] David Knight Lynch and William Charles Livingston, *Color and Light in Nature* p 261, p 268.

Bibliography

Bligh Bond & Lea, *Gematria*, London, 1977.

Bonnie Gaunt, *The Stones and the Scarlet Thread*, Kempton, USA, 2001.

Chris Morton and Ceri Louise Thomas, *The Mystery of the Crystal Skulls*, London, 1997.

David Knight Lynch and William Charles Livingston, *Color and Light in Nature*, 2001.

D.G. Leahy, *Foundation: Matter the Body Itself*, Albany, 1996.

Graham Hancock, *Fingerprints of the Gods*, New York, 1995.

John Michell, *The Temple at Jerusalem : a Revelation*, Glastonbury, 2000.

Marke Pawson, *Gematria*, Sutton Mallet, 2004.

Richard Heath, *Matrix of Creation*, London, 2002.

Steve Marshall, *Exploring Avebury The Essential Guide*, 2016.

William Stirling, *The Canon, An exposition of the Pagan Mystery perpetuated in the Cabala, As the Rule of All Arts*, 1897.

Index

208

R

Radius ratio 9
Rainbow 23, 103, 106, 162, 164-166
Rainbow Principle 162, 165
Ratio 5, 42, 58, 94
Reality 8, 53, 145, 146
Realm 104
Reason 135
Rectangle 15, 25
Rectangular 148
Reed 86, 91, 92, 152
Regeneration 103
Regular polygons 4, 58, 59, 129, 136
Reincarnation 103
Remainder 112, 115
Republic 94, 124
Resonance 10
Revolutions 45, 62, 69
Rho 86, 87
Rhombic dodecahedon 5, 7, 161
Rhombus 7
Rock 80
Rod 92
Rosslyn Chapel 46
Royal Cubit 91, 92, 108, 124
Ruben 19, 20, 85

S

Sacred Angle 66, 109
Sacred Geometry 38, 48, 108
Sacred symbol of Mu 18
Sagittarius 20, 151
Sanctuary 25, 26, 152, 155
Sapphire 152
Saqqara 6, 117
Sardius 152
Sardonyx 152
Sarsen 73
Saturn 87, 88, 103
Scale 27, 28, 35, 42, 78, 86, 124, 132
Scarlet 152
Scarlet Thread 108, 152
Science 8, 34, 42, 46, 50
Scientist 1
Scorpio 19, 20, 150, 151
Scotland 46

Scripture 82, 86, 124, 149
Seed of Life 28-30, 31, 37, 79, 101, 102, 131
Seed pattern 32
Seven pointed star 11, 16, 66, 106, 109, 111
Sheen Nun Yod 152
Shell 47
Shemhampohorash 46
Sigma 134
Silver 103
Simeon 20, 85
Simon 142
Sine 55-57, 159
Six pointed star 118
Sky 98, 154
Slope angle 11, 42, 95, 106, 108, 121, 123, 147, 155, 161
Slope side 139
Small cubit 92
Snail 36, 47
Socket 22
Solar system 75, 125
Solar year 6
Solomon 1, 13, 20, 25, 26, 74, 91, 109, 150-153, 155
Solstices 98
Son of Man 84
Soul 8, 18, 38, 101, 103
Sound 8, 46, 49, 53, 129, 132, 136, 157
Space 24, 133
Spaceships 145
Space-time 5, 10, 13, 28
Speed of light 79, 81, 93, 99, 121, 124, 157, 161, 166
Sphere 40, 42, 48, 49, 78, 82, 88, 89, 105, 106, 108, 133, 134
Spherical coordinates 38, 52
Sphinx 125
Spin 27-29, 33, 36, 45, 51, 53, 69, 75, 98
Spiral 26, 36, 39, 47, 74, 111, 112, 114, 115, 118, 135, 47, 143
Spirit 19, 65, 84, 94, 109, 126, 150, 153
Spring equinox 98

Made in the USA
Monee, IL
16 February 2023

27962677R00138